Understanding Alcoholism

Understandin

FOR THE PATIENT, TH

Compiled and edited b

New Yor

*

Alcoholism

FAMILY, AND THE EMPLOYER

Frazier, C. P. (handwritten)

The Christopher D. Smithers Foundation, Inc.

Charles Scribner's Sons

Grateful acknowledgment for permission to reprint material is made to the following:

Alcoholism & Drug Addiction Research Foundation: excerpts from *The Alcohol Language with a Selected Vocabulary* by Mark Keller and John R. Seeley, Brookside Monograph No. 2, 1958.

The American Management Association, Inc., and Harrison M. Trice: excerpts from "New Light on Identifying the Alcoholic Employee," *Personnel* (pp. 18–25, Vol. 41, 1964).

American Medical Association: excerpts from the 1966 Reaffirmation of the 1956 statement: Recommendations for the Admission of Alcoholics to General Hospitals.

Selden D. Bacon and The American Academy of Political and Social Science: material from "Alcoholics Do Not Drink" by Selden D. Bacon, *The Annals,* January 1958.

Foreword

This volume succeeds admirably in presenting a highly informative and panoramic view of alcoholism—that many-sided malady which, in one way or another, adversely affects almost every human activity in the Western world. But the various writers represented do far more than generalize. The alcohol problem is specifically seen from the vantage points of their personal observations or particular academic disciplines.

Alcoholism is here portrayed as having numerous causations. One portrayal describes components of social and family maladjustment, leading to neurosis, and thence to the bottle. Another explains compulsive craving, doubtless rooted in faulty metabolisms, and demanding alcohol for a dubious relief. Nor have moral and spiritual factors been overlooked; the lack of these values is recognized as often being a cause, as well as a result, of the alcoholic's woes. There is also a general understanding that any, or all, of these causations may be at work in any given case. Alcoholism is seen in its many combinations and degrees of illness as an affliction of the spirit, of the emotions, and of the body.

This comprehensive outlook on the illness already appears capable of rationally educating the alcoholic, and indeed all those who may become interested in him. It provides a real foundation for further education, research, and treatment—even for prevention.

Most importantly, these pages tell what today's treatments for alcoholism are, and where and how they can be obtained. This is valuable information for the alcoholic, his or her family, and his or her community.

It is most refreshing to see in these contents a truly open-minded approach. No contributor quarrels with another; no professional suggests that his particular discipline has anything like complete answers. The time has gone by when each of those specializing on alcohol problems seemed separated by communication-proof compartments. Today, all points of view can be heard and respected, no matter how divergent.

We of AA have likewise been lacking in open-mindedness. We, too, had our communication-proof compartment in which we were heard to declare that AA was the only solution. But that phase of our infancy is pretty much in the past. Our thoughtful members now well understand that we of AA are but a part of the great synthesis of meaningful forces now in formulation, a synthesis hopefully designed to cope on every front with the total problem of alcoholism. We therefore stand ready to cooperate with all constructive efforts in the field to the full extent of our ability. We AA's can now truly say "that in isolation we shall be limited but in cooperation with our friends, all may become possible."

That, too, is the spirit of this volume; it is a significant step in precisely that direction.

W. G. W.
Co-founder, Alcoholics Anonymous

Preface

The Christopher D. Smithers Foundation is a private charitable foundation incorporated under the laws of the State of New York in 1952, which has as its main objective helping to combat alcoholism. The Foundation is neither "wet" nor "dry"; it is solely interested in helping to establish alcoholism as a treatable disease, as officially recognized by the American Medical Association in 1956.

During the centuries of man's history, alcoholism has always borne a stigma in public opinion. Only a few years ago, cancer and tuberculosis also carried stigmas, but this handicap in fighting the latter two diseases has fortunately decreased in recent times. Medical scientists have thereby been given greater public support in their attempts to lessen the death toll of these diseases. While the stigma attached to alcoholism has lost some of its force in recent years, many people still consider the illness as weakness of character or moral dereliction.

As far as the Smithers Foundation is aware, it is the only working foundation in this country principally engaged in fighting alcoholism as a disease. We sincerely hope others will join us in the near future. This vital health problem is far beyond the scope or the financial means of one private group.

A large part of the material assembled for this book has appeared in a series of pamphlets, most of them written by Charles P. Frazier, Director of Education, the Smithers Foundation, and published by the Foundation, beginning in 1959. The primary objective of these publications was to create awareness and knowledge of alcoholism as a widespread illness among men and women of all social and economic backgrounds and to provide some understanding of its complexities.

The Foundation has consistently pointed out that alcoholism is treatable by modern methods. Over the past twenty years, thousands of people suffering from the disease of alcoholism have been able, through proper treatment, to resume healthy and productive lives. A wider public understanding of alcoholism can be expected to result in an increase in constructive action on the part of those afflicted to help themselves.

This is the goal of the Smithers Foundation and the objective of this book.

R. BRINKLEY SMITHERS
President, The Christopher D. Smithers Foundation

Contents

Understanding Alcoholism

* 1

THE ALCOHOLISM COMPLEX

On March 1, 1966, President Lyndon B. Johnson said, in his Message to Congress on Health and Education:

> The alcoholic suffers from a disease which will yield eventually to scientific research and adequate treatment. Even with the present limited state of our knowledge, much can be done to reduce the untold suffering and uncounted waste caused by this affliction.
>
> I have instructed the Secretary of Health, Education and Welfare to appoint an Advisory Committee on Alcoholism; establish in the Public Health Service a center for research on the cause, prevention, control, and treatment of alcoholism; develop an education program in order to foster public understanding based on scientific fact; and work with public and private agencies on the State and local level to include this disease in comprehensive health programs.[1] *

This succinct and matter-of-fact statement by the President of the United States not only sums up the attitude toward alcoholism now held by most authorities; it also dramatizes a change in attitude which has largely taken place in the past thirty years. With the appointment on October 20, 1966, of the National Advisory Committee on Alcoholism, reporting to the Secretary of Health, Education, and Welfare, the national government—rather belatedly—joined most of the state governments and various pri-

* Numbers refer to the Reference Notes at the back of the book.

vate and voluntary organizations in recognizing alcoholism as a major public health problem to be dealt with cooperatively through research, education, and medical treatment.

In October 1967 the Cooperative Commission on the Study of Alcoholism, established in 1961 under a grant from the National Institute of Mental Health, published its first report.[2] Among other recommendations, the Commission, whose seventeen members include psychiatrists, biochemists, and administrators, urged the creation of a committee for national alcohol policy under the Department of Health, Education, and Welfare to develop programs for a national attack on the disease. Says the Commission, "Heart disease, cancer, schizophrenia, and delinquency are not completely understood either, yet a community which responded to these conditions as it does to problem drinking would be considered medieval and a national disgrace."

Historically the attitude of the American public toward the condition now generally designated as alcoholism has been very different. The typical concept of the alcoholic was symbolized by the tragicomic figure of the red-nosed skid-row bum, derelict, homeless, irredeemable—an object of scorn and derision. In religious thinking this stock character was regarded as a sinner; in social and economic thinking as useless, hopeless, and without character. Both attitudes were held by the temperance movement which brought about national Prohibition in 1919.

As recently as the 1930s, a majority of American citizens held the belief that respectable people did not become alcoholics. If a man did not drink like a gentleman, he was sooner or later considered beyond the pale of social existence. If a woman (heaven forbid!) was suspected of drinking to excess, her shocked relatives soon withdrew her from public contacts.

The era of Prohibition paradoxically made drinking fashionable. The cocktail party became a symbol of social status, men and women frequented speakeasies together, and women openly drank "hard spirits" in public places—behavior never known in our history. But these revolutionary changes in public and private drinking behavior during the 1920s and 1930s did not extend to any change in the public concept of the alcoholic.

During the early 1940s, however, people in many communities became aware of the existence of an informal organization, whose members, former alcoholics from various social strata, openly admitted their condition and worked together to remain sober and to help others do so. They could point to many members who had returned permanently to sober and constructive lives. The program was something of a mystery to outsiders, but an important part of it centered around the concept that alcoholism was a disease. The members believed that they were allergic to alcohol and therefore for them total sobriety was the only cure. The movement, which was started in 1935 in Akron, Ohio, by a former stockbroker and a doctor, both alcoholics, spread gradually. During the 1930s small groups came into being in Cleveland, New York, Philadelphia, and elsewhere. The organization had no name until 1939, when a book recounting the experiences of some hundred members was published. Its title, *Alcoholics Anonymous,* was adopted as the name of the movement and was soon abbreviated to "AA." AA attracted widespread attention during the 1940s, not only in the United States but in Canada and abroad. The present membership is estimated at more than 400,000, and over 14,000 local groups are now functioning in some 90 countries.

Also during the 1940s articles by medical and science writers dealing with the idea that alcoholism is a disease began to appear in magazines and newspapers. The subject was occasionally discussed on radio programs. Social workers, public health nurses, and members of the clergy who attended the Summer School of Alcohol Studies at Yale University brought the new concept back to their communities. After 1945 local committees on alcoholism, composed of private citizens and business leaders as well as professional people, came into being in an increasing number of American cities and towns and in many cases operated information centers where people could discuss problems of alcoholism confidentially and without charge. These committees were affiliates of a voluntary organization, the National Committee for Education on Alcoholism (later the National Council on Alcoholism).

But the stigma attached to alcoholism died hard in the public mind. In 1948 when J. W. Riley, Jr., of Rutgers University in a nationwide survey [3] questioned a representative sample of men and women on their opinions on alcoholism, only 20 percent of those questioned regarded an alcoholic as a sick person, while 58 percent saw no difference between an alcoholic and a person who gets drunk frequently. Furthermore, 50 percent of those interviewed thought that alcoholics did not require treatment but could stop drinking if they wanted to.

Ten years later, Elmo Roper and Associates conducted another nationwide survey, reported in a newspaper release in January 1958. To the question "If you knew someone who habitually drank so much that it affected his job and his relations with people, would you say he is morally weak or would you say that he is sick?" the distribution of answers was: morally weak, 35 percent; sick, 58 percent; no opinion, 7 percent.

This tremendous increase in acceptance of the concept of alcoholism as an illness in the short span of ten years is highlighted by the press reaction to a speech made in October 1959, at a dinner given in New York City to celebrate the fifteenth anniversary of the founding of the National Council on Alcoholism. The speaker, Secretary Arthur S. Flemming of the United States Department of Health, Education and Welfare, stated that more than 5 million men and women were suffering from alcoholism in the United States and that these people, coming from every walk of life, had a disease. He pointed out that, contrary to the general public impression, the great majority still have homes, jobs, and financial means and he said that they constitute one of this country's four greatest public health problems.

A few years earlier, such statements by a leading government official would have drawn indignant protests from both editors and newspaper readers. But many leading newspapers published Secretary Flemming's remarks next day without comment, considering them newsworthy because they had been made by a United States Cabinet member, not because the Secretary had regarded alcoholism as a medical problem rather than a moral weakness. By 1959 the concept of alcoholism as an illness had been accepted by a great many Americans.

This reversal in public opinion seems to have been brought about chiefly by the work of the organizations already mentioned, all of which constantly emphasized the "new approach" to the old problem. However, many people still questioned this premise, regarding it as "an excuse for lack of personal control." Though a lessening of the stigma attached to alcoholism became increasingly noticeable, the controversy about the nature of the condition continued throughout the 1950s.

In 1957 The Christopher D. Smithers Foundation undertook to clarify this controversial situation by making a grant to Dr. E. N. Jellinek (1890–1963) for research on a world-wide basis on the whole alcoholism problem. An internationally known authority, Dr. Jellinek was a co-founder and former director of the Yale Center of Alcohol Studies and had served as a consultant on problems of alcohol for the World Health Organization in Geneva. Three years of extensive research resulted in the publication of his book *The Disease Concept of Alcoholism*, which has since become a classic reference work in the field. Since Dr. Jellinek's ideas are fundamental to any consideration of the disease nature of alcoholism, a condensation of parts of his book constitutes the remainder of this chapter.[4]

History of the Disease Concept

The phrase "new approach to alcoholism" was coined around 1940 and has been widely used. Actually "renewed approach" would be a more correct expression. In the late eighteenth and early nineteenth centuries the American Surgeon General Dr. Benjamin Rush and the British physician Dr. Thomas Trotter wrote on "inebriety" as an illness, though their ideas did not bear fruit for sixty or seventy years. In the 1830s Dr. Samuel Woodward, first superintendent of the Worcester (Massachusetts) State Hospital, and Dr. Eli Todd of Hartford, Connecticut, as well as the Connecticut Medical Society, suggested special institutions for inebriates—a recognition that inebriety should not be classed with either criminal behavior or mental disorder—and a French social investigator, Dr. A. Fregier, opposed the penal attitude toward inebriates.

The Washingtonian Home for inebriates first opened in Boston in 1841. Between that date and 1874, at least eleven nonprofit hospitals and homes for inebriates came into existence in the United States. Noteworthy among these was the New York City Asylum, opened in 1869, operated by the Police Department and the Board of Charities of New York City. The superintendents of these early special institutions, on the basis of their experience, soon gave voice to the slogan that "intemperance is a disease."

They even founded a society for the study of inebriety and in 1876 began to publish *The Journal of Inebriety,* which existed (although precariously) for about thirty-eight years. After Dr. Sigmund Freud visited this country it described itself on the masthead as "the first and only journal devoted to spirit and drug neurosis." But *The Journal of Inebriety* and the society never made a dent on the public at large or even on the medical profession. The strong temperance movement then prevalent in the United States rejected the idea of inebriety as a disease since this weakened the basis of its own ideology. By the era of national Prohibition, the *Journal* had ceased publication. The interest of American scientists in the problems of alcohol waned and the American public was interested in the problems of bootlegging, not in the problems of alcoholism. Lack of interest over many years relegated to oblivion the efforts of the early proponents of the illness conception, but somehow the idea that alcoholism is an illness was still hovering in order to be rediscovered.

Over the years since the repeal of Prohibition, interest in problems of alcohol and alcoholism revived, and the conception of alcoholism as a disease became not only a working hypothesis in research and in the clinical treatment of some varieties of alcoholism but also the central point of certain community activities related to the problems of alcohol. The renewed idea found its way not only into professional circles but far into public opinion, until now in America one may speak of a majority acceptance of the illness conception of alcoholism.

Most influential in bringing about this acceptance seem to have been the complex of activities at Yale University, the National Council on Alcoholism and its local affiliates, the Committee on Alcoholism of the American Medical Association, the state government agencies, and the fellowship of Alcoholics Anonymous.

Experiments on alcohol metabolism, begun in the 1930s in what was then the Laboratory of Applied Physiology at Yale, led by 1940 to a program of coordinated research which attracted representatives of the medical, biological, and social sciences, as well as of the law. *The Quarterly Journal of Studies on Alcohol,* the Yale Center of Alcohol Studies, and the Yale Summer School of Alcohol Studies [now held at Rutgers University],* were among the results of the program. The illness conception was central to the activities of the Summer School, which was originally developed for interested laymen. Its students, many of whom were in strategic positions, carried their new knowledge back to their communities.

The Yale group also lent its sponsorship in the early stages to the voluntary lay organization for education on alcoholism founded by Mrs. Marty Mann, which was later to become the National Council on Alcoholism, and which, along with Alcoholics Anonymous, achieved the widest spread of the idea that alcoholism is an illness. However, in the long run neither of these groups could have maintained its influence without support from the medical profession, as exemplified by the AMA's Committee on Alcoholism. The activities and achievements of these various groups led state governments to set up programs for the treatment of alcoholism as a public health problem. In 1956 the AMA formally accepted the concept that alcoholism is a disease, a move which marked a tremendous step toward national public acceptance of the idea.

However, since alcoholism has too many definitions and disease has practically none, the old vagueness still adheres to the

---

* Square brackets are used to enclose necessary editorial additions and explanations to clarify previously published text.

new concept, and if it is not clarified the gains of the illness conception may be lost again. Nevertheless, the idea would not have spread so widely if there had been no significant clarification, although the multiplicity of hypotheses may still confuse the public. To some extent, the differences in the hypotheses denote the fact that there is not one alcoholism but a variety.

[After the completion of *The Disease Concept of Alcoholism*, Dr. Jellinek illustrated this contention with a botanical comparison: "After looking over the whole world, I am convinced that alcoholism is a genus, not a species. . . . Everyone knows the hibiscus flower—there are over two hundred species. As to genus, *hibiscus* comprises herbs, shrubs, and trees. The botanist will ask: Which hibiscus are you referring to? So alcoholism can be considered: which alcoholism are you talking about? Some may be disease, some may be symptoms of a disease, others may be neither diseases nor symptoms, but habits."]

The species of alcoholism must be stated definitely and with stringent criteria. There are certain species of alcoholism of which one can legitimately ask: Are they diseases?

The present vagueness surrounding the whole conception of alcoholism is dangerous because of its continuance. The formal acceptance of the disease conception by the AMA does not mean that acceptance among physicians is unanimous, although the majority of American physicians are either in agreement with the dictum of the professional body or are willing to accept this viewpoint on the authority of their specialized professional colleagues. Quite a proportion of physicians will be inclined to think of alcoholism rather as a symptom of an illness than as an illness per se. Perhaps a majority of those who accept the illness conception have vague ideas about its nature, particularly as many of its medical proponents have themselves indulged in vagueness.

Business management and organized labor in the United States have increasingly tended to accept the concept of alcoholism as a disease, and their cooperation to insure the effectiveness of programs for the rehabilitation of alcoholic employees has been an important element in public acceptance. But, as far as management is concerned, the disease idea of alcoholism may be nothing more than a convenience in tackling the vexatious problems of alcohol, and the belief in the disease conception actually does not go very deep with the majority. To both labor and management, the idea of alcoholism as a disease was rather welcome, as this is one of the questions on which they could easily meet. Most unions, however, argue that alcoholism should be considered as an illness subject to the same benefits and considerations as more commonly recognized illnesses.

The public attitude remains of paramount importance for various aspects of the problem of alcoholism. The acceptance or rejection of the idea determines to a large extent whether or not the general public will have hope and therefore also the incentive for the rehabilitation of alcoholics.

Furthermore, the continuation of public and voluntary agencies concerned with alcoholism depends upon the moral and, to some extent, the financial support of the aggregate of citizens, and this support, in turn, depends upon the attitude of the public toward conceptions about the nature of alcoholism.

In spite of the high degree of acceptance by the public at large, the belief may not be deeply rooted as yet. Much of it may be lip service, repeating what has been heard on the radio or at a lecture given by someone who attended the Yale Summer School of Alcohol Studies, or read in a pamphlet, or heard from Alcoholics Anonymous friends. That the belief is of no particular depth may be attributed to the vagueness of the formulations of the disease conception that reach the general public. The picture of alcoholism behind the acceptance is perhaps that it is "something mental" and perhaps that an allergy to alcohol is involved, although in medical and scientific circles the latter theory is the least accepted.

Generally, it may be said, not only of the medical profession, industry, and labor, but of all the other sections of public opinion that their feeling is that the idea that alcoholism is an illness is true, but not really true. This feeling will persist until the disease conception of alcoholism attains to clarity and definitiveness.

However, a disease is what the medical profession recognizes as such, and the fact that doctors are not able to explain the nature of a condition does not constitute proof that it is not an illness. There are many instances in the history of medicine of diseases whose nature was unknown for many years. The nature of some is still unknown, but they are nevertheless regarded as unquestionably medical problems. The medical profession has officially accepted alcoholism as an illness, and through this act alone it has become an illness, whether a part of the lay public likes it or not and even if a minority of the medical profession is disinclined to accept the idea.

But acceptance does not equal validity, and one may inquire into this latter point, particularly into the matter of the facts and ideas that lie behind the illness conception, that is, into the nature or natures of some species of alcoholism. The difficulty in this instance is that the proponents of the still somewhat vague illness conception operate with many concepts which either are not defined or are frequently used in a variety of connotations. Such, for instance, are the concepts of tolerance, craving, habituation, sensitivity, compulsion, habit-forming drug, withdrawal symptoms, loss of control, and so forth. And there remain the definitions of alcoholism and the alcoholic, as well as of the term "problem drinker," all of which are used in a variety of meanings.

In order to clarify to some extent the cultural, social, and economic factors in the problems of alcoholism as they tend to complicate the question of the illness conception, an excursion must be made into other parts of the world.

Alcoholism in Other Countries

The etiquette of American alcoholism literature demands that the psychiatrist should acknowledge that physiopathological, cultural, and social elements have a role in the genesis of alcoholism. On the other hand, the physiopathologist is required to admit the existence of social, cultural, and possibly some individual psychological factors. With few exceptions, however, specialists, after having made the prescribed bow, proceed to formulate their theories of causes exclusively in terms of their respective disciplines. Thus, the idea that presents itself to an omnivorous reader of the alcohol literature is usually that alcoholism is an economic, a psychological, a physiological, or a sociological problem, to the exclusion of the other aspects. Such is the impression even after the perusal of a book in which representatives of the various branches of science collaborate.

As the majority of the students of alcoholism, including the sociologists, mention alcoholism as an illness or the symptom of an illness, one may be somewhat confused as to whether it is a personality disorder, a physical illness, or, figuratively speaking, a disease of economic life, of social structure, or of culture.

The greater part of the newer literature on alcoholism is of American and British origin. In these two nations the steady "problem drinkers" and the "true alcohol addicts" are so much in the foreground, and engage the interest of the student of alcoholism to such a degree, that the terms "alcoholic" and "alcoholism" are applied only to those drinkers, and the problem is seen entirely in terms of their drinking.

Drinking patterns vary in various countries and they can determine the course of the alcoholic process of the individual. In a wine-drinking country, such as France, where wine is often drunk throughout the day, the drinking pattern can lead to a constant presence of alcohol in the body with little manifestation of overt intoxication. This results in a variety of addiction in which there is no "loss of control" (over the amount of alcohol taken), but instead an inability to abstain. On the other hand, in the Anglo-Saxon countries there is, as the majority rule, no distribution of alcohol over the entire day but rather a shocklike impact of strongly intoxicating liquors toward evening. This pattern can produce loss of control but leaves the ability to go on the water wagon (abstain for shorter or longer periods) practically intact.

The addict of the "inveterate" type (as the French wine drinker) has no guilt feeling about drinking, usually has no difficulties with himself, his family, or others—in other words, does not experience those tribulations to which the majority of British and American alcohol addicts are subjected. The difficulty experienced in establishing Alcoholics Anonymous groups in Latin countries is probably largely due to the differences in the experiences of their alcohol addicts from those in the Anglo-Saxon countries. The ideology of Alcoholics Anonymous does not find an echo in the experiences of the French inveterate addicts, who in that country form the majority of alcoholics. That French majority type is in America a minority type; it may be that at least some of the alcoholics who drop out of Alcoholics Anonymous here belong to that type. A review of the international scene leads to the conclusion that in many countries more serious problems of national magnitude arise from other types of drinkers than from those who in this country are termed "alcoholics." The latter type does, of course, exist in every country where alcoholic beverages are consumed, but it may form a small group or, even if its numbers are fairly large, the problems arising from it may be overshadowed by the problems which the other types of drinking present.

There is a condition referred to by French students of alcohol problems as "*alcoolisation.*" A large number of drinkers who are neither psychologically nor physically dependent upon alcohol have such a large daily consumption that their life span is shortened. An economic factor also plays an important role in France in relation to alcoholism; because of pressure of vested interests [the wine industry], it is extremely difficult to establish legal and educational controls or even to launch a nationwide campaign for the public care of alcoholics. The slightest mention of anything of this nature provokes vigorous antagonism not only from the vested interests but also from the majority of the population.

Various Species of Alcoholism

Through adherence to American ideas about alcoholism and alcoholics, many problems of alcohol which need urgent attention have been overlooked. While in American alcoholism literature, by and large, an alcoholic means a true addict—the type prevalent in Alcoholics Anonymous—a number of American students of alcoholism would include under that term heavy weekend drinkers, as well as "relief drinkers" who never become addicted.

To do justice to international as well as to American differences, alcoholism may be defined as any use of alcoholic beverages that causes any damage to the individual or society or both. Vague as this statement is, it approaches an operational definition.

It may be said that such a loose definition has little operational value. With such a vague definition one cannot even ask whether alcoholism is an illness. Obviously there are species of alcoholism—so defined—which cannot be regarded as illnesses. One may well say that such a vague definition is useless. But in this uselessness lies its utility, for it forces us to single out species of alcoholism (in the preceding sense) and to speak of them in stringent terms. We must be particularly definite about those forms which we wish to examine as possibly constituting illnesses. Furthermore, in view of our broad and vague statement of alcoholism, we cannot say that alcoholics are those who suffer from alcoholism as so defined. We shall have to make a distinction between alcoholism and alcoholics.

In discussing the species of alcoholism and alcoholics brief descriptions will be given and labels attached without any pretension to formal definitions. Only those species of alcoholism that may come into consideration as disease processes or symptoms of disease processes will be described and labeled. For the labeling of the species of alcoholism considered here, letters of the Greek alphabet have been used.

Alpha alcoholism represents a purely psychological continual dependence or reliance upon the effect of alcohol to relieve bodily or emotional pain. The drinking is "undisciplined" in the sense that it contravenes such rules as society tacitly agrees upon—such as time, occasion, locale, amount, and effect of drinking—but it does not lead to loss of control or inability to abstain. The damage caused by this species of alcoholism may be restricted to the disturbance of interpersonal relations. There may also be interference with the family budget, occasional absenteeism from work and decreased productivity, and some of the nutritional deficiencies of alcoholism, but not the disturbances due to withdrawal of alcohol. Nor are there any signs of a progressive process.

The relief of bodily pain or emotional disturbance implies an underlying illness and thus the "undisciplined" use of alcoholic beverages may be regarded as a symptom of the pathological conditions which it relieves. This species of alcoholism cannot be regarded as an illness per se.

Of course, it is quite possible that in many instances alpha alcoholism may develop into gamma alcoholism. On the other hand, it is well known that this species of alcoholism may be seen in a drinking career of thirty or forty years without any signs of progression. Alpha alcoholism here means this latter "pure culture," not the developmental stage of gamma alcoholism.

Alpha alcoholism as described here is sometimes called problem drinking, but that expression just as frequently includes physical dependence upon alcohol. The terms "problem drinking" and "problem drinker" will not be used in this chapter.

Beta alcoholism is that species of alcoholism in which such alcoholic complications as polyneuropathy, gastritis, and cirrhosis of the liver may occur without either physical or psychological dependence upon alcohol. The incentive to the heavy drinking that leads to such complications may be the custom of a certain social group in conjunction with poor nutritional habits. The damage in this instance is of course the nutritional deficiency diseases, but impaired family budget and lowered productivity as well as a curtailed life span may also occur. Withdrawal symptoms, on the other hand, do not emerge.

Beta alcoholism too may develop into gamma or delta alcoholism, but such a transition is less likely than in the instance of alpha alcoholism.

Gamma alcoholism means that species of alcoholism in which are involved: (1) acquired increased tissue tolerance to alcohol, (2) adaptive cell metabolism, (3) withdrawal symptoms and "craving" (physical dependence), and (4) loss of control. In gamma alcoholism there is a definite progression from psychological to physical dependence and marked behavior changes.

Gamma alcoholism is apparently (but not with certainty) the predominating species of alcoholism in the United States and Canada, as well as in other Anglo-Saxon countries. It is what members of Alcoholics Anonymous recognize as alcoholism to the exclusion of all other species. AA uses loss of control and craving as the criteria par excellence, but these necessarily involve the other characteristics of gamma alcoholism already mentioned. Naturally AA has created the picture of alcoholism in its own image, although at least 10 to 15 percent of the membership are probably specimens of alpha alcoholism who conform in their language to AA standards. This statement is based on the fact that in a sample of slightly over 2,000 AA members, 13 percent had never experienced loss of control. More likely than not, only a small percentage of those with alpha alcoholism would seek the help of Alcoholics Anonymous, and almost none of those with beta alcoholism. The latter may be seen most frequently in general hospitals (see Appendix A). In spite of the respect and admiration to which AA has a claim on account of its great achievements, there is every reason why the student of alcoholism should emancipate himself from accepting the exclusiveness of the picture of alcoholism that this group has propounded.

Delta alcoholism shows the first three characteristics of gamma alcoholism as well as a less marked form of the fourth characteristic—that is, instead of loss of control there is inability to abstain. In contrast to gamma alcoholism, there is no ability to abstain completely for even a day or two without the manifestation of withdrawal symptoms; the ability to control the amount of intake on any given occasion, however, remains intact. The incentive to high intake may be found in the general acceptance of the society to which the drinker belongs, while pre-alcoholic psychological vulnerability, more often than not, may be of a low degree. This species of alcoholism and its underlying drinking pattern were described in connection with the predominant species of alcoholism in France and some other countries with a large wine consumption. Delta alcoholism would rarely be seen in Alcoholics Anonymous, since the alcoholic afflicted with this species of alcoholism does not go through the distressing social and psychological experiences of the gamma alcoholic and manifests only a few of the behavior changes of the latter.

There are, of course, many other species of alcoholism—defined as any drinking that causes damage—and all the remaining nineteen letters of the Greek alphabet, and if necessary other alphabets, are available for labeling them. Among these other species is periodic alcoholism, which in Europe and Latin America is still designated as dipsomania, a term now in disuse in North America. It may be denoted as *epsilon alcoholism* but as it seems to be the least-known species it is neither described nor defined here. In the course of their periodic bouts, epsilon alcoholics may cause serious damage. In the last twenty or twenty-five years a phenomenon which may be called "pseudoperiodic alcoholism" has turned up. Apparently some gamma alcoholics, who have not benefited to the full extent from the AA program or from therapy in clinics or by private psychiatrists, are able to resist drinking for three, six, or twelve months but then find no other solution than intoxication, after which they remorsefully return to sobriety.

Other species of alcoholism (accepting the criterion of damage through drinking) include "explosive drinking," as well as *alcoolisation* (the undermining of health and curtailing of the life span without physical or psychological dependence). Then there is the excessive weekend drinking which follows a cultural pattern and causes damage through rowdiness, absenteeism, and impairment of the family budget. Still other species cause damage; for instance, "fiesta drinking" and occasional drinking that causes accidents. The student of the problems of alcohol cannot afford to overlook these behaviors, whether or not he is inclined to designate them as species of alcoholism.

Species for Consideration as Diseases

Returning to the question of whether alcoholism is a disease, only alpha, beta, gamma, delta, and epsilon alcoholism can come into consideration at all. Alpha alcoholism may be ruled out, as it is the symptom of an underlying disturbance; this of course does not deny that the person suffering from this species of alcoholism is a sick person. As to beta alcoholism, it too must be ruled out, being neither a disease per se nor even a symptom, unless we regard the drinking that produces the damage (certain alcoholic diseases) as social pathology, a rather diffuse concept. No doubt polyneuropathy, cirrhosis of the liver, and gastritis are serious diseases, but in this instance they are purely effects of the excessive drinking, and in this species the excess in drinking itself does not indicate any physical or psychological pathology and no dependence develops.

This leaves the gamma, delta, and epsilon species of alcoholism. The first two of these may come into consideration as diseases, since it is the adaptation of cell metabolism, the acquired increased tissue tolerance, and the withdrawal symptoms, which bring about "craving" and loss of control or inability to abstain. These species involve that use of alcoholic beverages which induced Selden D. Bacon [Director of the Rutgers University Center of Alcohol Studies] to say "alcoholics do not drink," although Bacon was thinking not merely of the loss of control, but quite rightly, of some drinking behaviors which precede the loss of control.[5] In gamma alcoholism, the adaptation of cell metabolism and the other characteristics already mentioned indeed represent physiopathological changes analogous to those in drug addiction as well as psychopathological conditions which differ from those of any possible pre-alcoholic psychopathology. With the exception of the psychological changes and the loss of control, which is replaced by the inability to abstain, the same changes are involved in delta alcoholism.

If it should be conceded that morphine, heroin, and barbiturate addiction involve grave physiopathologic processes which result in "craving," then these addictions may be designated as diseases (and they are included in the American Medical Association's nomenclature of diseases). The gamma and delta species of alcoholism may be so regarded by the same tokens (and alcoholism is included, too, in the list of the AMA). Of course it is a matter of opinion whether or not such processes are designated as diseases. On the other hand, the presence of the physiopathological changes leading to craving cannot be denied in the addictions, whether to narcotic drugs or alcohol. The current majority opinion is that anomalous forms of the ingestion of narcotics and alcohol, such as drinking with loss of control and physical dependence, are caused by physiopathological processes and constitute diseases.

Whether epsilon alcoholism—that is, periodic alcoholism—is a disease per se or the symptom of an underlying disease cannot be asserted at the present state of knowledge. Pseudoperiodic alcoholism or pseudo epsilon alcoholism is a relapse into a disease, but the occasion for the relapse is a voluntary one and does not form a part of the disease process, except perhaps in a psychopathological sense.

The definition of alcoholism as any drinking which leads to any damage does not permit designating as alcoholics all those who on occasion create some kind of damage through their use of alcoholic beverages. The present study defines as alcoholics only those who manifest the alpha, beta, gamma, delta, and epsilon varieties of alcoholism. This is admittedly an arbitrary distinction. Some may wish to exclude the alpha or beta alcoholics or both, and others may be inclined to include the explosive drinkers, the alcoholized (*alcoolisé*) drinkers, or perhaps all who cause any damage through any use of alcoholic beverages.

Definition of Terms in Alcoholism Literature

In the alcohol literature the term "loss of control" (over the intake of alcohol) is frequently used interchangeably with the expression "uncontrolled drinking." Quite often, however, different drinking behaviors are designated by these two terms.

Recovered alcoholics in Alcoholics Anonymous speak of loss of control to denote that stage in the development of their drinking history when the ingestion of one alcoholic drink sets up a chain reaction so that they are unable to adhere to their intention to have one or two drinks only but continue to ingest more and more—often with quite some difficulty and disgust—contrary to their volition.

However, the loss of control does not emerge suddenly but rather progressively and does not occur inevitably as often as the gamma alcoholic takes a drink. The loss of control becomes fully established several years after the first intoxication.

In the writings of quite a number of students of alcoholism, the expression "uncontrolled drinking" does not denote the behavior just described but rather a deliberate transgression of the social rules (admittedly diffuse rules) relating to amounts, times, occasions, and locales of drinking. In order to avoid the suggestion of loss of control in this latter drinking behavior, the expression "undisciplined drinking" seems to be more appropriate, particularly since the drinker in these instances is not deprived of free choice. This undisciplined drinking is characteristic of the alpha alcoholic, but it occurs in the gamma alcoholic too before loss of control is established. Paradoxically enough, after the establishment of loss of control, deliberate undisciplined drinking greatly diminishes in the gamma alcoholic, as he knows or is afraid that the loss of control might bring about serious consequences in situations where that behavior would be most dangerous. As the loss of control progresses, however, the attempt to discipline the drinking occasions may break down.

The loss of control extends over a given drinking bout, after which the gamma alcoholic is able to abstain from alcoholic beverages for shorter or longer periods. His starting a new bout is not ascribable to the mechanism of loss of control nor to compulsion, but rather to an impulse whose danger either is not recognized or is explained away.

The delta alcoholic, on the other hand, is unable to abstain entirely for even a day or two, although he can control the amounts he consumes on any given occasion. Loss of control and inability to abstain are thus not interchangeable terms.

It may be said that an "overpowering desire"—that is, a physical dependence upon alcohol—is shown only in the presence of withdrawal symptoms, and these are late developments in gamma and delta alcoholics. At the beginning of their drinking careers the prospective gamma alcoholics undoubtedly show a greater desire for the tension-reducing effects of alcoholic beverages than do other users of alcohol, but they do not seem to give any indication of an initial physical dependence. Any theory of causation which postulates pre-alcoholic physiopathological factors that lead from the very start to a larger-than-average intake of alcohol must give evidence that such an intake constitutes craving in the sense of physical dependence upon the substance.

The term "compulsion" is frequently used to denote the same drinking behavior which is designated by many as "craving." Psychiatry and psychology offer only nominal definitions of compulsion—namely, that which impels an act contrary to the conscious will. In the sense that a physical dependence can cancel out the conscious will, it is not unreasonable to designate as compulsion the behavior manifested in loss of control. But since the term compulsion is, as a rule, regarded as a psychopathological phenomenon it does not seem to cover behavior which arises from the need to alleviate such distressing manifestations as withdrawal symptoms.

"Tolerance" to alcohol may be defined as a critical level or threshold of alcohol concentration in the blood at which measurable changes occur in nervous functions. A distinction must be made between inherent or initial tolerance and acquired increased tolerance. The terms "tolerance" and "intolerance" in relation to alcohol have been used indiscriminately to designate a variety of phenomena, among them the loss of control. [In this chapter the term tolerance is used exclusively as defined here.]

"Habituation" to alcohol is a term which is frequently used synonymously with tolerance to alcohol but just as frequently to denote the process of physical dependence. Furthermore, habituation and forming a habit often become entangled. This state of affairs is confusing and the term habituation will not be employed here except when quoting or paraphrasing writers on this subject.

"Sensitivity" to alcohol is invoked as a factor by some students. Those who use this term take for granted that what it means is understood and consequently do not define it. The use of the expression "sensitivity" sometimes creates the impression of some esoteric concept. Occasionally this term is used to denote tolerance. Some students of alcoholism speak of sensitivity when they mean that certain individuals are not able to resist the ingestion of alcohol. It seems preferable to avoid this term entirely, particularly as one can do quite well without it. /

"Susceptibility" is one of the vague characteristics referred to occasionally in the etiology [study of the causes] of alcoholism. Susceptibility means a state of mind in which the individual shows particular readiness to avail himself of the use of a certain substance or to engage in a certain activity. Of course, a person who is suffering from stresses and lacks the ability to cope with them is more "susceptible" to the use of a tension-reducing substance, such as alcohol, than a well-balanced person. The use of the term "susceptibility to alcohol" contributes little if anything to the description of the alcoholic process unless the term is greatly elaborated. Occasionally, as with sensitivity, the factor of susceptibility acquires a mystic character through the omission of definition. /

Ethical Involvements

Although the disease concept of alcoholism requires elucidation in terms of psychological and physiological formulations, the existence of ethical questions in this area cannot be overlooked. In the view of the Roman Catholic Church, "abuse" rather than drinking is the sin. This is also generally the view of the Anglican Church, the Eastern Orthodox Churches, the Lutherans with the exception of some synods, and a few other Protestant churches.

The Roman Catholic moral philosopher Father John C. Ford expresses the Catholic attitude thoughtfully and eloquently:

A great many alcoholics (especially the secondary addicts) begin their drinking by way of harmless self-indulgence. But this indulgence soon becomes so attractive that it leads to sinful excess. Sins of deliberate drunkenness become habitual. Little by little one moral ideal after another is allowed to grow dim. Honesty goes. Humility goes. Purity goes. Increasing selfishness and egocentricity, increasing self-deception; increasing neglect of family, business and friends. . . . At all events my experience and their own estimate of themselves after they recover leads me to the conclusion that most of them undergo that process of moral deterioration for which they are in varying degrees responsible. I call this a sickness of the soul. . . .

But supposing alcoholism to be a pathological condition, is it a condition for which the alcoholic himself is responsible? Objectively, many alcoholics are little responsible for their condition either because their addiction has a physiological basis over which they never had control, or because, as in the case of certain primary addicts, they were compulsive drinkers almost from the beginning. They are spoken of sometimes as addictive personalities. They consider themselves to have been alcoholics from the moment they took their first drink, and they are right. . . .

Again, objectively, many other alcoholics are responsible for their condition because it is the result of long-continued excessive drinking for which they were responsible. To the extent that they foresaw addiction as the end-result or probable end-result of their excess they are responsible for not having prevented it.

But subjectively, it seems to me, not many alcoholics are morally guilty as far as the addiction itself is concerned. Very few foresee addiction. Very few believe that they will ever become drunks. There is nothing more insidious and blinding than alcoholic excess. Men and women who are beginning to drink too much are warned by their friends what will happen to them. But they do not believe it. They are convinced that they are going to be different from the horrible examples that are pointed out to them. They succeed in deceiving themselves. Add to this the general ignorance about the nature of alcoholism and the moral confusion with which the majority of them consider the question of excessive drinking itself.

. . .

Although the alcoholic may be powerless over alcohol, and unable at times directly to resist the craving for drink, yet it is within his power, generally speaking, to do something about his drinking. He is therefore responsible for taking the necessary means to get over his addiction.[6]

For the elusive question of alcoholism as a self-inflicted condition Father Ford's discussion must suffice. Any longer exposition of the matter would not diminish the elusiveness except for those who have definitely made up their minds on this question.

Less elusive, but still not quite in the sphere of clear-cut judgments, is another ethical aspect of all species of alcoholism. This is the fact that the prospective alcoholic (in whom the disease process has not started as yet), instead of putting out a constructive intellectual and emotional effort to cope with tensions, is taking recourse to the pharmacological effects of a drug which either gives the illusion of having done something about the causes of the tension or alternatively crowds these causes out from the contents of his awareness.

In this instance, too, some mitigating elements must be considered. One is that the drug used is, as one may say, a domesticated drug to which society has attached a certain prestige value. Another is that the incipient addict for a long time is not aware of the use to which he is putting alcoholic beverages. For considerable periods the incipient alcoholic associates his feeling of well-being not with the ingestion of the alcoholic beverage but rather with the circumstances under which such ingestion takes place —that is, with certain localities and the companionship of certain persons and, perhaps, with some activities to which drinking is incidental. It is quite some time before it dawns upon the incipient alcoholic that it is the alcoholic beverage which affords him relief and even then he tends to persuade himself that that is not the case.

The World Health Organization's Committee on Alcohol and Alcoholism designated ethyl alcohol as a drug "intermediate in kind and degree" between "habit-forming drugs" and "addiction-producing drugs."[7] Their reasons for assigning alcohol to this intermediate position were largely the quantitative differences between alcohol and the addiction-producing drugs. The latter produce addiction in 70 to 100 percent of their users, the amounts required to bring about this effect are minute, and the time required for the addictive process is two to four weeks. Alcohol consumption, on the other hand, leads to addiction in a maximum of 10 percent of the users, requires large amounts (several thousand times larger than morphine, heroin, or barbiturates), and the time necessary for the addictive process is three to fifteen years, in some cases over twenty years.

Some Reasons for the Social Acceptance of Alcohol

The drug ethyl alcohol is contained in such "respectable" ancient beverages as beer and wine, as well as in the relative newcomers brandy, whisky, and other distilled spirits. Furthermore, these beverages are socially highly valued and their use has a tremendous acceptance in quasi-social ritual and as a "dietary supplement."

The great social acceptance of the alcoholic beverage may be attributed first to its symbolic value and second to its effects.

Strangely enough, students of alcoholism have not paid attention to the symbolism of the alcoholic beverage; not even psychoanalysts have touched on this aspect. On the other hand, classical philologists and students of the comparative history of religion interested in the sacrificial and other ritual use of wine or other alcoholic beverages have shown the equation between the alcoholic liquid and blood. They have done this without reference to the social or "dietary" custom of drinking. The deep symbolic meaning of the act of drinking—irrespective of whether water, milk, or an alcoholic beverage is consumed—has been explained as the taking in of the "stream of life." [8]

There are many Greek, Roman, medieval, and later literary passages that bring out the symbolic character of the alcoholic beverage, particularly the meaning of drinking together as an act of identification, much more clearly than the ritualistic material referred to by the students of comparative history of religion.

Through the equation of alcoholic beverages with blood, some of the properties of the latter are transferred to the former; not only those of strength, power, and renewal of life but also those of food and medicine. These transferred symbolic properties endow the alcoholic beverage with that tremendous prestige which has led to the extraordinary wide acceptance of the custom of drinking in a large variety of cultures. The symbolism of the alcoholic beverage gives it its anchorage in society. The act of identification in drinking together is the root of the offense inherent in the refusal of a drink, and generally of social pressure to drink.

That the custom of drinking alcoholic beverages has maintained itself in the face of many changes in social and cultural structure, and in spite of the realization of potential dangers, is due not solely to the deep symbolic value of alcoholic beverages but also to their "utility." Nevertheless, the utility alone, without the prestige of the symbolism, could not account for the survival of the custom with its many vexatious problems.

Development of Alcohol Addiction

Of course persons with great psychological vulnerability may be much more motivated to use the tension-reducing properties of alcohol more frequently and in greater quantities than others. The relatively small percentage of persons who become addicted to alcohol, compared to morphine, heroin, and other drugs, may be attributed to the relatively small incidence in the population of those who have an urgent motivation to take alcohol in the large quantities and with the frequency that is required to bring about physical dependence on alcohol through conditioning of the metabolism of nervous tissue. This in no way precludes a true addictive process in persons with low alcohol tolerance—persons who become intoxicated after drinking small quantities of alcohol. In spite of their "alcohol intolerance" these persons may consume prodigious quantities.

The utilitarian use of alcohol—that is, for its effects—by no means necessarily leads to excess and some species of alcoholism. Persons with minor tensions and ample resources to manage those tensions engage in utilitarian drinking in small amounts only, and, according to the culture to which they belong, in connection with meals (either just before or in the course of eating) or on certain social occasions.

Nor should it be thought that excessive drinking necessarily produces addiction. There may be heavy, frequent drinking which does not go beyond psychological dependence but still may cause social damage and damage to the user's health, and thus may be seen as the alpha species of alcoholism.

In spite of a great diversity of personality structures among alcoholics there appears in a large proportion of them a low tolerance for tension coupled with an inability to cope with psychological stresses. For such persons alcohol may represent a "great value" which may induce them to use this substance in such quantities and with such frequency that the pharmacological process of addiction is facilitated. The addictive process may develop without initial psychological dependence, but in a large proportion of gamma alcoholics pre-alcoholic high psychological vulnerability is essential.

Given a large and frequent intake of alcoholic beverages, whether for individual psychological reasons or on account of socioeconomic factors, the exposure to the risk of addiction in the pharmacological sense becomes great.

In gamma alcoholics it is the gradual, slow development of the loss of control which generates the dramatic behavior changes. The loss of control, even in its earlier less obtrusive forms, brings about a feeling of insecurity on account of the gradual narrowing of choice for the individual concerned. When the addictive process is on its way, the role of the person diminishes and alcohol takes the upper hand as the nervous tissue becomes gradually conditioned by that substance. Progressively alcohol "takes over" until it becomes the decisive factor in what the addict may or may not do. Thus the slogan "alcoholism is not in the bottle but in the man" may be a dangerous one.

A Working Hypothesis

The various psychological and psychiatric explanations of alcoholism may fully account for the heavy drinking which paves the way for addiction, but not for the great changes, the progressions, and the loss of control as they occur in gamma alcoholism. The same is true of sociocultural explanations, although drinking patterns inherent in certain cultures may play a role in the conditioning of the cell metabolism (particularly in the genesis of delta alcoholism).

In America, where the therapist is predominantly concerned with the gamma alcoholic, the main structure around which research should center is the pharmacological process of addiction. While the process of addiction is not a full explanation of gamma and delta alcoholisms (not to speak of other species of alcoholism), it constitutes a convenient axis of research for the following reasons:

The time necessary for the development of addiction may, as previously stated, vary from three years to fifteen years and even longer in persons who are equally heavy users of alcoholic beverages.

Enzyme and vitamin anomalies, liver injuries, adrenal factors, and many biochemical lesions known at this time may according to their various degrees weaken the resistance of nervous tissue to the integration of a noxious substance into its metabolism and to becoming dependent upon it. If any physiological or biochemical anomaly—which in itself may not seem grave—can strip the nervous tissue of its resistance to adaptation of its metabolism to a noxious substance, then that adaptation with all its accompanying behavioral changes may be designated as a disease.

Such anomalies and injuries could be products of heredity, or they could be brought about through the stresses which prolonged heavy alcohol intake may exert on them. In view of the varying length of time in the establishment of the addictive process, heredity may play a role in the time necessary for alcohol to exert serious stresses on the system to which the anomaly attaches.

Moreover, the absence of such anomalies could account for the phenomenon of alpha alcoholism, in which very heavy alcohol intake, in spite of marked drunkenness, does not produce any progression, particularly no transition from psychological to physical dependence.

This working hypothesis is one which can be tested by means of the newer techniques in pharmacology, physiopathology, and biochemistry. Some of the profitable targets of research are the process of acquired increased tissue tolerance and the mechanisms of the various withdrawal symptoms.

The Illness Concept in Other Countries

The great propaganda effort practiced in the United States for the acceptance of alcoholism as an illness is largely absent in European and South American countries. In those countries, there are few if any voluntary agencies concerned with alcoholism, except temperance associations. On the other hand, such activities have been initiated recently in Australia, New Zealand, and the Union of South Africa, where voluntary agencies have been organized on the pattern of the National Council on Alcoholism.

Generally speaking, European nations, especially those countries that have compulsory treatment of alcoholics, have less need for the acceptance of these ideas by the public at large. The decisive factor in such countries is acceptance by the medical profession and by government welfare agencies. Nevertheless, where the basis of public care of alcoholics rests on the illness conception of alcoholism, the propagandization of that idea might result in greater effectiveness of public care, particularly through the voluntary acceptance of treatment by the early alcoholics.

In Canada, at present, nearly all provinces have alcoholism programs which embrace the illness conception of alcoholism. This is particularly true of the programs of Ontario, Manitoba, Alberta, and British Columbia. Voluntary agencies, in the United States sense, do not exist in Canada. Most of the provincial "alcoholism foundations," however, have grown out of citizen endeavors which through public subsidy have become either semiofficial or fully official agencies but do not come under public administration. Most of the Canadian alcoholism programs publish magazines or newsletters as well as a large number of pamphlets which strongly emphasize alcoholism as an illness. Although the Canadian alcoholism programs show a great deal of originality, the impress of the Yale Center of Alcohol Studies is evident. This is quite natural, as most of the administrators of the provincial alcoholism programs are former students of the Yale Summer School of Alcohol Studies.

From the Canadian medical literature it would appear that the medical profession as a whole has a favorable attitude toward the disease conception. While an official recognition such as that given by the American Medical Association has not come forth from the Canadian medical group, the ties with the AMA are so close that the latter's pronouncements carry considerable weight in Canada too.

The repercussions of the provincial alcoholism programs are, in some way, more marked than those of the state programs in the United States. This is demonstrated by the adoption of the illness conception by the Canadian Civil Service and the Royal Canadian Air Force, both of which have made that conception a basis for dealing with alcoholic members of their groups. To what degree the Canadian public at large has accepted these ideas cannot be expressed statistically at present. It may be inferred, however, that the wide publicity which the illness conception has received in the press, frequent radio programs, television, and educational films all over the country, must have brought about an increasing recognition of the idea. Also, next to the United States, Canada has the largest Alcoholics Anonymous membership and thus a strong contingent of zealous propagandists.

The Medical Profession's Attitude

Earlier in this chapter it was pointed out that as long as the propagation of the disease conception of alcoholism was limited to a small specialized professional group, the idea did not penetrate public opinion and was noticed only by the temperance movement, which rejected it. In the instances of tuberculosis, cancer, heart disease, and mental health, to bring the teachings of the medical profession closer to the public at large, propaganda through the channels of voluntary citizens' groups was required and still is. This does not mean that the attitude of the medical profession is not important in this matter. Quite the contrary—if the medical profession were not to accept the idea of alcoholism as an illness, the movement for its propagation would sooner or later collapse.

An essential requirement is that the first proponents of the idea be members of the medical profession. In the beginning, it is not necessary that the medical profession as a whole should adopt the suggestion, although later an official stand of the profession as such becomes necessary. In the case of alcoholism, the idea that it constitutes an illness was suggested to Alcoholics Anonymous by a physician, the late Dr. W. D. Silkworth, early in the 1930s. Behind this physician were the opinions of a fair number of American and European specialists as expressed in the course of some sixty or seventy years, although their views did not coincide with the particular conception of Silkworth—that certain people have an allergy to alcohol. It cannot be said that at that time the medical profession as a whole was in agreement with the medical proponents of the disease idea, yet the number of physicians of the latter conviction was not negligible. The spread of the disease conception of alcoholism to much wider circles of physicians was due not only to the somewhat greater precision of the formulation of the idea, to experimental findings, and to new therapeutic methods such as administration of Antabuse, but also to the efforts and ideology of Alcoholics Anonymous whose members were propagating with the greatest vigor what they thought was a new conception.

The official acceptance by the medical profession of the disease conception of alcoholism is required not only for the continued life of its propagation through citizens' groups but also to encourage a much larger number of physicians to acquire experience in the treatment of acute intoxication, alcohol addiction itself, and the various organic and mental complications. Medical acceptance is also essential in order to induce hospitals to accept alcoholics for treatment, as hospitals in general had developed admission policies that excluded the alcoholic and such policies were often upheld by the boards of trustees.

Furthermore, medical acceptance is fundamental to a policy of subsidies for clinical activities and research work in the field of alcoholism by the large foundations. Such foundations have in the past quite understandably hesitated to make grants for research and clinical work and educational activities relating to alcoholism. As medical acceptance increases, the foundations may feel reassured and make significant grants, particularly for alcoholism research and education.

The acceptance by hospitals of alcoholics as legitimate patients has made great strides since 1944, when a survey showed admission of alcoholics to general hospitals much more the exception than the rule.[9] Another study of the same year stated: "Most of our hospitals have failed thus to dignify alcohol addiction as a disease worthy of study and intensive care."[10] Since then the reports of state and voluntary agencies show that hospital attitudes have undergone considerable change, although not enough. [For later developments in this area, see Chapter 7, pages 180–185.]

Importance of the Disease Designation

A European authority stated in 1929 that it is an idle pastime to ask whether alcoholism is an illness or not; the main thing is that something should be done for the rehabilitation of the alcoholic.[11] This is the kind of epigrammatic utterance that, at first glance, meets with the great approval of the reader. On reflection, however, this dictum might not prove to be very cogent. It may not be of particular importance whether certain species of alcoholism are labeled as illnesses or designated as medical problems, but the acceptance of either of the two labels, or the rejection of both, has a very definite bearing on many aspects of the problems of alcoholism. The consequences of such acceptance or rejection are reflected in such matters as whether ideas on the rehabilitation of alcoholics will be orientated toward therapeutic, social welfare, or penal measures. "Concern over the confusion with regard to alcoholism as a symptom or a disease may appear to be a product of the academic mind, but the position taken on this matter determines the orientation of therapeutic efforts. If . . . alcoholism is regarded as a symptom, then the treatment program is designed to cure the underlying disease." [12] The latter approach is in contrast to that of Alcoholics Anonymous, which regards addictive drinking itself as an illness and directs its efforts toward breaking up the sequence of activities involved.

The rejection or acceptance of alcoholism as an illness or a medical problem may have repercussions not only in rehabilitation methods but also in the extent of clinical activities and other medical facilities for alcoholics. Furthermore, the degree of acceptance may affect the research in various aspects of alcoholism. "A more fundamental reason why research on alcoholism has not achieved the degree of biological perspective available for research on tuberculosis, cancer, poliomyelitis, is the slow development of the concept that alcoholism is a disease." [13]

A low degree of acceptance of the disease conception may handicap subsidization of biological research on alcoholism, but, on the other hand, the vagueness of the conception is a stimulus to the development of clearer formulations and more stringent experimental research. Research, treatment, and prevention of the various species of alcoholism are affected not only by the acceptance or rejection of the disease conception, but also by the formulation of the nature of such an illness. If the formulation rigidly claims that alcohol addiction or any other species of alcoholism is purely a medical problem, any preventive attempt may be seriously impaired. The usefulness of the idea that alcoholism is a medical and public health problem depends, to a large extent, upon the recognition of social and economic factors as causes in all species of alcoholism. By recognition of these factors is not meant mere assent that such factors exist but exploration and understanding of them.

Many factors play a role in the degree of acceptance or rejection, among them the clarity and definiteness of the formulations. It must be admitted that clarity is not an outstanding characteristic of any but a very few of the formulations. And definiteness is, of course, lacking when vehement controversies concerning theories are rampant. The lack of clarity is, at present, not too great a deterrent for public acceptance of the disease idea, but in the course of time it may become a very serious handicap.

Some elements influencing the matter of acceptance or rejection lie in deeply rooted traditions about the custom of drinking which cannot be divorced from the phenomenon of alcoholism. Much depends upon the extent and quality of propaganda which attaches to alcoholism as an illness or, if one prefers the term, to education on alcoholism. The way in which these conceptions fit into the sociopolitical ideas of some interest groups is, of course, also of relevance.

The question of what formulation of the illness conception is accepted by and large by one or the other section of public opinion cannot be determined on the basis of existing information. The indications for the great majority are that the accepted version is merely that "alcoholism is a disease." For the time being this may suffice, but not indefinitely.

* 2

A PROGRAM FOR ARRESTING
ALCOHOLISM

In the present state of knowledge of the complex designated as alcoholism, it is not realistic to talk of "curing" the disease. However, there is now a considerable body of evidence to show that it can be arrested permanently if the victim is able to avoid drinking. The gamma alcoholic of Dr. Jellinek's classification (see Chapter 1), who is both psychologically and physically "hooked" by alcohol, represents the type commonest in the United States and is the type to which the term alcoholic in this chapter refers. For the rehabilitation of such alcoholics, a set of practical suggestions has been developed from the experiences of many who have arrested their dependence. These suggestions are primarily directed to those for whom the only course presently known is complete abstinence. For these people, knowledge of the nature of the disease is essential.

One definition of an alcoholic is "a person whose drinking frequently interferes with his business, his social life, or his health." Usually it is safe to say that a person who is continuing to have trouble with alcohol in any department of his, or her, life is well on the way toward alcoholism.

If such a problem exists for a normal, or social drinker, a stop is soon made, through either curtailment or abstinence. The problem is not allowed to continue and grow (for the alcoholic's problem rarely remains for long at the same level—it grows progressively worse). Even so-called heavy drinkers (a far different category from alcoholic drinkers) soon cut down to normal quantities of alcohol, or cut it out entirely, when any continuing trouble arises. For the heavy drinker the element of choice exists: he is able to control his drinking if and when he chooses.

Early Warning Signs

Recovered alcoholics looking back on their drinking careers agree that there were certain warning signs of oncoming alcoholism. Since most early drinkers know nothing of the nature of alcoholism, these warning signs almost invariably went unheeded. If understood, they might have revealed a growing preoccupation with the pampering effects of alcohol. Almost without exception, the recovered alcoholics mention their immense satisfaction with the effects of alcohol—what drinking "did for them." If they were shy, drinking gave them self-confidence and made them more outgoing. If they tended to be introverted, alcohol made them extroverts, even sometimes the life of the party. Drinking also overcame feelings of inferiority.

Peculiarly, many alcoholics report that in the beginning they had a tremendous capacity for alcoholic beverages; they were known to their fellows as having a "hollow leg," often ending a party by helping to take their more sensitive drinking companions home. It was only after years of progression that this seeming imperviousness vanished and they could no longer drink "normally."

The great majority of recovered alcoholics also state that their preoccupation with drinking began early in their drinking careers. No party, football game, or social event was complete without drinking.

One symptom, however, goes beyond the early warning stage. Any person who is experiencing "blackouts" (losses of memory for certain periods of drinking) should realize that this tendency invariably signals a state of alcoholism.

Once a person has crossed the invisible line which separates so-called normal drinking from alcoholism, he or she has almost certainly lost control forever. While an alcoholic can attempt controlled drinking and succeed for varying periods of time, in the end he goes overboard—usually at a most inauspicious time. The only safe assumption is that long-term controlled drinking is not possible for any drinker who has become an alcoholic.

Are You an Alcoholic?

If one wishes to determine whether or not one might be an alcoholic, the most sensible way is to seek the advice of those skilled in the complexities of alcoholism as a disease. Consult with one of the local alcoholism information centers maintained throughout the United States by the affiliates of the National Council on Alcoholism; or the state and provincial tax-supported alcoholism programs in the United States and Canada. Or visit the open meetings of the nearest group of Alcoholics Anonymous. Talk with AA members, all of whom have gone through the experience of doubt and perplexity over their drinking but have found a successful solution. (See Appendix D.)

Finally, think over the definition on the first page of this chapter; then test yourself honestly with the self-analysis questions in Appendix B. Then sit down in a quiet room and think.

For anyone who is seriously looking for a way to stop drinking, the absolutely essential first requisite is to want to do so for one's own sake. To think of stopping for someone else's sake is not enough; you must stop because of your own selfish best interests. If this sounds cynical, keep on drinking. Eventually even those closest and dearest to you will wash their hands of the whole affair and drop all contact with you. They will have to do this for their own good. An alcoholic can produce more personal grief for those around him than any other human being. The patience of Job would have been sorely tried by an alcoholic.

However, when one has been a fairly consistent drinker for some time, one doesn't give up the habit easily. You cannot just turn off the spigot and quit. There will be occasions when you are depressed and say, "What's the use—let's have some drinks!" Or you may be elated and want to celebrate. To guard against such happenings, you must educate your subconscious mind to withstand the temptation when it comes. Halfway measures such as limiting yourself to a glass of beer or sherry are no good at all. To quit effectively you must quit entirely.

The speed and facility with which the desire for alcohol is eliminated depends more than anything else on the individual's conception of the importance of his problem. A man who can keep permanently before his eyes the fact that he wants to stop drinking because his entire future depends on it, and that therefore this subject is of supreme importance, will discover that the attainment of his goal is far easier than he anticipated. On the other hand, anyone who thinks that the question is relatively inconsequential, that he can be careless in his application of constructive methods, or that the treatment is of secondary importance to something else, will find giving up the habit next to impossible.

Tampering with the Human Mechanism

The majority of alcoholics would instantly follow the strictest instructions regarding their daily life if they were warned by their physicians that they had some acute organic illness—heart disease, cancer, or tuberculosis—which would soon lead to suffering and death if they continued their former ways of life. Alcoholism is as destructive and dangerous as heart disease, cancer, or tuberculosis. One must understand that the very fact that he cannot drink normally is a definite danger in itself and that a persistence in the use of alcohol will probably lead to serious mental and physical complications.

The extreme nervousness, depression, and physical illness which occur in the "hangover" of those poisoned by alcohol can perfectly well become permanent if the mind and body are subjected to too many alcoholic shocks over a long period of time.

Doctors who work in the field of alcoholism will corroborate this statement from actual experience. In every state mental hospital are numbers of patients suffering from what doctors call "wet brain." Physical check-ups reveal evidence of permanent physical damage in many patients who are chronic alcoholics.

Men drink alcohol because it stimulates and relaxes simultaneously. Although ethyl alcohol is popularly considered a stimulant, actually it is a sedative. It creates a feeling of self-confidence and self-importance, while it soothes, calms, and gives poise. The elation which comes from drinking is the result of a fusion of these two effects.

The alcoholic, because of the poisonous effect that alcohol has on his nervous system, must have the patience to learn to relax naturally, and to achieve poise through legitimate, constructive forms of self-expression rather than through alcoholic fantasies. He must strive to make real life such that he is content to live in it and not be perpetually trying to blot it out with a drug. Alcohol as used by the alcoholic is much more akin to narcotics than to the social stimulant that it is supposed to be. The chief difference is that alcohol is easier to obtain; no prescription is needed.

The true and complete picture of the effects of drinking must be faced continually. It cannot be emphasized too often that for an abnormal drinker alcohol has become and will remain forever an antisocial narcotic drug, to which he has become an addict.

Drinking, Past and Present

Most abnormal drinkers have been through a stage of normal drinking earlier in their lives. As a result, they persist in striving to bring back the good old days, naïvely clinging to the idea that they can do so despite continuous and dramatic proofs to the contrary. This preposterous and childish self-deception is the cause of a great deal of trouble. The drinker must recognize that now, in contrast to his earlier experiences, alcohol definitely undermines his nervous system, psychologically and physically poisons him, and attempts to reproduce normal indulgences are and always will be futile. His reaction to alcohol has radically changed, and a continued attempt to "drink like a gentleman" will only aggravate his present condition. No man whose response to alcohol has been of a pathological nature can afford to drink at all.

No one will ever stop drinking if he waits for an ideal time to begin. There is nearly always some situation (which one may or may not have brought on oneself) which is disagreeable but which apparently cannot be changed—at the moment, anyway. One must realize that the more unpleasant the predicament the more he will profit by abstinence, because of the extremely depressing aftereffects of drinking. The excessive use of alcohol will always make a bad situation worse. Intoxication can never be a satisfactory avenue of escape from trouble. But reorganization of personality has been accomplished by a great many people whose situation was far from enviable, and who achieved results not because of the easiness of their lives, but in spite of its difficulties.

Medical Help

Many persons feel absolutely unable to stop drinking because their physical hangovers are so severe and the withdrawal symptoms are impossible to bear "cold turkey." In such cases, the drinker should consult a doctor for a course of treatment which will make it possible to stop drinking without too much suffering.

Physicians, psychiatrists, and other medical specialists can help the alcoholic who wants to stop drinking and eventually maintain sobriety.

First, a thorough medical check-up is recommended. Since alcoholism is a serious illness, hospitalization is often necessary, especially in chronic cases. A competent doctor familiar with the problems of alcoholism will supervise the patient's treatment during the period of withdrawal. He will prescribe the proper medication and other medical care needed at this time. Even when hospitalization is not necessary, the medical examination often reveals other needs. Many alcoholics suffer from malnutrition after protracted periods of drinking; the doctor will prescribe the proper diet and vitamin intake to rectify this deficiency. A check-up may also disclose the presence of other ailments which had been masked by the alcoholic symptoms or been neglected during the drinking period.

During the later stages of rehabilitation, psychiatrists or psychologists are often of great help in showing the alcoholic how to achieve a mental adjustment to a new life without alcohol. Most people who drink too much, either temporarily or continuously, have personality problems. Consultation with a trained psychiatrist has helped many alcoholics to recognize these inner problems and learn to deal with them. However, the psychiatrist must be told of the patient's alcoholic background at the start of the consultation. In many instances, a combination of steady attendance at AA meetings and regular visits to a psychiatrist knowledgeable in the nature of alcoholism has been the means of building a solid, long-term happy sobriety.

Attendance at group-therapy meetings and participation in psychodrama [acting out roles or incidents] under the direction of a skilled psychiatrist have also been of great assistance to many alcoholics.

Some leading doctors who have been very successful in treating alcoholism recommend the daily use of Antabuse, a drug which will induce extreme nausea if alcohol is ingested into the system, even in minute amounts. This drug has proved a strong deterrent to impulse drinking, especially during the first year or so of sobriety. Antabuse or any other drug should always be used under a doctor's direction. While the use of such a drug is a daily reaffirmation of the desire to stop drinking, for best results the practice should be combined with regular attendance at AA meetings or group-therapy classes.

Honest Self-Appraisal

To be absolutely honest with oneself is just as important and for most people a great deal more difficult than to be so with others. The childish element in human nature can be very skillful at times in its effort to have its own way—for example, to take a drink. Often one must assume the role of detective in order to bring the various subterfuges, rationalizations, and sophistries to consciousness in their true light before they have a chance to do harm. Any reasoning that seems to lead to a reduction of effort in carrying out the treatment prescribed to arrest alcoholism should be thoroughly and honestly scrutinized before it is accepted as a basis for action.

For most people there have been times when actual performance in some important aspect of life has not even approximated the ideals they envisaged. The failure was rationalized (a form of self-deception in itself), and the rationalization may have served as an excuse to the outside world. Deep down in the individual's own consciousness, however, the failure resulted in a loss of self-confidence and perhaps a growing feeling of inferiority. In the new life the aims are to raise one's sights and at the same time choose goals in which one's ideals are attainable.

Every time you are doubtful about whether a contemplated action is wrong or right, stop and consider whether the risk is worth taking. If you "get caught" can you take the consequences? Most importantly, can you bear the possible guilt or remorse without being driven to drink again? Such considered meditation beforehand often avoids serious consequences, not only for oneself but also for others who may be involved. At the very least, it brings into play solid honesty with your own inner self.

Do It for Yourself

As has been pointed out, there must be no doubt whatsoever that the problem of giving up drinking primarily concerns yourself, and that you will accomplish very little in the long run if you view it in any other light. If you wish to succeed, your actions must in no way be contingent upon the conduct of others. The happiness that permanent sobriety will bring to your friends and relatives is a good secondary reason for giving up drinking, but the primary reason is your own good. You must believe that to stop drinking is the expedient thing to do and that you, more than anyone else, will profit from your abstinence and suffer from your indulgence.

The ideas of friends and relatives are often ignorant and hence as useless as they are well intentioned. You must disregard suggestions about taking a drink once in a while, or such questions as, "Why do you need to be shown how to stop doing something that nobody is compelling you to do?" People who have never been seriously affected by alcohol themselves (and this most certainly includes normal drinkers) cannot be expected to have a sympathetic and constructive understanding of the problem. Their unintelligent comments must not be allowed to discourage or divert you from your original purpose.

Experimentation

This section is for the "early" alcoholic—the man or woman who has been experimenting with giving up alcohol. Troubles from drinking have taken place—not as serious as getting fired from a job, or a family break-up, but ominous in import. Perhaps there have been warnings at the job, disagreeable scenes in the family or in social life. Two or three "trial runs" of stopping drinking have been attempted over short periods but have ended in the resumption of drinking on a so-called controlled basis. Examples of this control are substituting wine or beer for "hard liquor," or refraining from alcoholic beverages during the day and taking only two drinks in the evening before dinner. Sooner or later, these experiments have failed, and new drinking problems have arisen.

Taken aback by the failure of the controlled-drinking theory, the drinker finally decides that total sobriety is for him. He may then decide to try Alcoholics Anonymous. Perhaps from almost the first meeting sobriety "catches on." Weeks and even months may pass without his drinking. The problem seems to have cleared up. The former drinker is highly elated. He or she has become active in an AA group; spends much spare time in helping sober up friends and others who have a similar predicament.

Overconfidence takes the place of a carefully developed program to ward off possible temptation. Then suddenly a crisis arises—usually of an emotional nature—and before the fledgling in sobriety realizes what has happened, he or she is drinking again, usually in even a worse fashion than before.

This situation may well represent the crossroads between the way toward a happy life on the one hand and skid row on the other. Relapses are serious events, like the loss of a crucial battle in a heretofore successful campaign. Their psychological impact is always shattering. Remorse to the point of extreme depression sets in; the unfortunate person loses whatever little power he ever possessed to give up alcohol.

If the alcoholic is able, after a short period of renewed drinking, to get back to whatever program for sobriety he or she has been following before the relapse, this may not prove serious. In some instances, consultation with a physician is in order. Vitamin injections may be necessary if vitamin deficiency or malnutrition has occurred during the drinking period. Tranquilizers may be employed to calm the nerves and induce the relaxation and sleep necessary for recuperation from the sudden physical shock of renewed drinking.

But when the renewed drinking has gone on for longer periods of time, during which malnutrition may have intensified the seriousness of the illness, immediate hospitalization is the wisest first step toward recovery. This decision may be on the alcoholic's own volition or at the insistence of relatives or friends. Proper hospital treatment, preferably in a hospital or rehabilitation center where other alcoholics are being treated, will quiet the nerves and clear the brain. After a week depression will lessen, making the person more amenable to trying again.

The prompt resumption of whatever program for sobriety the alcoholic has been pursuing is vital—just as the flier who has crashed *must* go up again immediately. Relapses are extremely dangerous. Veteran AA members can bear witness that some former members never recover from them; the progression of alcoholism hurls these drinkers downward at an accelerated rate.

The Right Start

The help of another person who has been through the mill of alcoholism and now leads a contented life of sound sobriety can be paramount in importance. Those who sensibly seek the help of AA are strongly urged to establish contact with a sound, sensible sponsor within the movement. Do not simply attend meetings as a "loner," one who sits in the back row at meetings and takes no part. While eventually AA's program for a new way of life usually does "rub off," provided one constantly attends meetings, the key to success is action. A sound and interested sponsor is a bridge to AA, and there are many such people available.

When an alcoholic gives up drinking, the pampering effects of alcohol are sorely missed at first, especially at those hours of the day which used to be occupied with drinking, say from five until seven in the evening. These intervals must not be left as a vacuum. Substitute some constructive action to fill them. Most people have outside interests beyond their jobs. Start a program in which you are really interested and which you may have intended to pursue for years past, even at moments during your drinking past. Before long you will find yourself involved in devoting an hour or two daily to something you always did well. You will become pleasantly conscious of gaining skills beyond those ever experienced heretofore.

Sound, constructive outside interests bring peace of mind, satisfaction, and above all self-respect. You will find yourself happier than you ever were when drinking. When you do, you are fairly safe on your course toward sound sobriety. You will also realize how time-consuming drinking can be, and how many hours have been wasted in the past. But do not allow regrets for lost time to overcome you. Remember the AA adage: "We can do nothing about the past, the future is yet to come, the important thing is the present."

Once you have had a reasonable period of sobriety, one of the most constructive kinds of action is to become a sponsor for other alcoholics. Your own sponsor can help you in this effort, and perhaps will work with you in helping others toward sobriety.

Excuses

Alcoholics are experts at fooling themselves, and any self-deception in regard to drinking must be checked immediately. The man who is earnestly endeavoring to stop drinking must understand that his entire future depends on complete abstention. He cannot afford to have any reservations which permit his taking a single drink. The problem is not one of dissipation but of a dangerous psychopathological drug. The abnormal reaction to alcohol is not so much a question of quantity as it is of effect. Since his early days of drinking the alcoholic's nervous system has undergone a radical change and a refusal to face this fact in a courageous and intelligent manner will result only in disaster.

Wish-fulfillment day-dreaming is not just a harmless way of passing the time. Nothing is more dangerous than the idea that "it does not make any difference how much I think about wanting to do a thing as long as I do not do it." It is essential to understand that thoughts are dynamic. They will express themselves in action unless they are inhibited by other, more powerful thoughts. So the man who is an alcoholic must continuously stress inhibiting thoughts. He must drive it home to himself over and over again that he does not want to drink and he does not intend to do so. Even more important, he must give himself as many arguments for the truth of these statements as his experience will permit. Conversely, he must reason away (not suppress) his old habit of thinking of alcohol as a means of acquiring happiness the instant he recognizes that such thoughts have entered his mind. If real temptation is encountered, he must bend all his energy toward diverting his mind through some form of immediate action.

Obviously, a man cannot take a drink unless he thinks about taking it first. But behind the act-producing thought is a long series of ideas, reflections, and suggestions stretching far back into the past. It is the control and redirection of this preliminary thinking that ultimately determine conduct. To tell yourself that you do not want to drink any more is not enough. You must support the statement over and over again with the wealth of material which you can draw from your painful experiences, so that each time the mind is diverted the unconscious is left with a complete picture of reality. Remind yourself that you have eliminated a serious problem and that you are not giving up anything.

Application of Will Power

In overcoming alcoholism there are two ways of applying will power: directly on the temptation itself and in carrying out the treatment. In the long run, people translate their desires into action, and so the crux of the situation is to change the desires. This can be done by conscientiously controlling and directing the mental processes over a long period of time. Thus, the larger field for the use of will power is in concentrating on mental training with the maximum of fidelity and vigor, and letting the states of mind that result from it take care of the situation. But if occasionally the desire to drink arises in spite of the best efforts at re-education to prevent this, will power must be used without stint directly on the desire, in the good old-fashioned way. There are other more legitimate desires that cannot be satisfied either. If one can accept these frustrations without whining, one can do the same about alcohol. The necessity for this direct use of will power will decrease as time goes on. Remember that the time to exert will power is before taking the first drink.

Launch with determination and vigor your decision to eliminate alcohol from your life. Then do all in your power to maintain this attitude with enthusiasm. Do not permit yourself to become bored and lazy; it is not necessary. The carrying out of your decision need not be monotonous. The reintegration of your character by the understanding and training of your mental processes can be an increasingly intriguing practice. From time to time you will make interesting and encouraging discoveries about your mind, and you will be agreeably surprised to find out how much of a mind you possess, once you have ceased to drench it with alcohol.

The best way to take care of future attitudes and conduct is to anticipate them with frequent reflection and suggestion. Successful results are obtained only through active cooperation.

Nothing can be done to help anybody who is not doing his utmost to help himself. Each individual has within him two elements —that of the doctor and that of the patient. If he did not have the first element, he would not have sought assistance; usually only those who fully recognize their problem and wish to take definite measures to correct it are suitable prospects for help. Therefore people can and must treat themselves in a vigorous and intelligent manner. The doctor element, no matter how small in the beginning, gradually increases with faithful effort, while the patient element correspondingly diminishes.

Relapses on the part of those who are sincerely trying not to drink are most likely to occur at a period of change, particularly when the change involves emotion. Therefore, such times should be given particularly careful attention. When possible, they should be prepared for in advance. Such changes are from happiness to sorrow or worry, from excitement to boredom, and their opposites. Changes of location, as well as of occupation, even if temporary, also require an extra amount of defensive preparation. Almost anybody can follow a routine without much difficulty, provided that it is not too monotonous for too long a time. But when external stimuli are suddenly changed, people are likely to be put off their emotional guard, and it is when their emotional balance is disturbed that they are most likely to succumb to any passing desire which may be aroused by an unaccustomed situation.

Wise planning with an understanding friend is a most important preliminary to a course of conduct. The sustained execution of a plan, however, is just as important. Once a course of action has been determined upon, execute it, unless you have a very honest reason for changing your mind. This applies not only to abstinence itself, but to the minor episodes of everyday life. The overcoming of alcoholism calls for sustained action. Words and theories which do not produce a continuously dynamic self-treatment are useless.

Food and Rest

The statements about the effect of change also apply to undue fatigue. The best preventives for the nervous, tired feeling which so often leads to drinking are exercise, food, and rest. The person in the process of eliminating the desire for alcohol must make sure always to eat something before he becomes too hungry, especially if his occupation is a fatiguing one. The end of the working day is a particularly important time to remember this. Something sweet is especially helpful. No one ever wanted a cocktail after eating a bar of chocolate. Do not excuse yourself from carrying out this valuable preventive measure on the ground that your appetite for a regular meal will be spoiled. A light dinner will do you no harm, whereas a drink will ruin you. Under no circumstances should you go without a meal or permit a doughnut and a cup of coffee to take the place of breakfast or lunch.

After a hard day at work, the time when many alcoholics were formerly accustomed to drinking can often be used for a good rest. This should be taken lying flat on your back with your clothes loosened. Whether or not you sleep is unimportant. After a half-hour or so, you will feel relaxed and perhaps a little "dopey." If you have to do something that evening, a showerbath, or even just washing your face and hands with cold water, will wake you up. You will feel much better than you did when you drank for strength to carry on planned activities.

Most alcoholics while drinking suffer from malnutrition. Alcohol is a unique substance in that, unlike most drugs, it can serve as a fuel for the body. It is double-barreled in its activity: it serves as a source of energy, like sugar, but at the same time it acts as a poison to derange the appetite mechanisms of the body, thereby destroying the appetite for food and inducing a physiological craving for alcohol. Since alcohol is an important source of calories, the person who has stopped drinking must replace this source of energy with food; he must learn to eat breakfast again.

The diet of the recovering alcoholic should contain a large amount of high-quality protein. This is found predominantly in meat, fish, poultry, eggs, milk, and cheese. Through consumption of protein foods, the alcoholic will inevitably get some of the minerals and vitamins that he needs. Fresh fruits and vegetables also contribute these. Cabbage, broccoli, Brussels sprouts, and carrots are of special value because of their relatively high content of calcium. Yellow vegetables contribute vitamin A in conspicuous quantities. Some nutritionists recommend a tablespoon of corn oil per day in the form of salad dressing. This is to furnish certain unsaturated fat acids which are essential in rebuilding physical fitness.

An alcoholic should avoid all refined foods. These furnish little or no minerals, vitamins, or high-quality protein. Food products which should be avoided or kept to a minimum include syrups, white rice, spaghetti, macaroni, and white-flour products (which never have all the vitamins and minerals restored). These refined food materials tend, as does alcohol, to crowd out of the diet items necessary for rehabilitation. If one leaves alcohol alone and restricts himself to good unrefined foods for a reasonable time, the body appetite helps to promote the eating of enough food to furnish these essentials. A vitamin supplement can also be helpful.

Medicine for the Spirit

A major destruction wreaked by alcohol is that of the individual's spirit. Cynical attitudes induced by long-continued drinking tend to wipe out any spiritual feelings the alcoholic originally possessed. A belief in a higher power of any sort is usually lacking, "Look what's happened to me," says the alcoholic. "Where is any God's handiwork in this mess?"

Arrested alcoholics often remark on the return to belief in some outside power greater than themselves, which occurs after a reasonable period of sobriety. Slowly but surely, as the miracle of contented sobriety evolves, many former agnostics become deeply spiritual, claiming that they could not have accomplished this major change without the help of a force beyond themselves.

How to Find Happiness in Sobriety

During the early stages of recovery from active alcoholism, the day-to-day schedule still retains many of the stresses, strains, and tensions, both physical and mental, which were familiar in drinking days. The newly sober person may well wonder at times how anyone who has been an active alcoholic can ever reach a state of comfortable and happy sobriety. The answer is persistence and patience. All of a sudden you begin to be concerned about others. At this point you forget your own problems. Your ego improves and this is the beginning of happiness.

Children may have learned during the course of the illness to disregard an alcoholic parent. It will take time for them to unlearn this. During the first year of sobriety, the children may act in ways that seem disrespectful. They have learned to turn to the sober parent as the authority in most things concerning the family. Naturally, the alcoholic resents the lost role, but he or she must be prepared to be patient with the children and give them time to recover their respect and love. As sobriety continues, this will occur. The recovered alcoholic should guard against temper outbursts and authoritative demands; these will only delay a change in the children's attitude.

The kind of indirect alcoholic suggestion that may come from identifying oneself with a character in a movie, play, television program, or book can be much more conducive than any cocktail party to a return to drinking. Such identification with a character who drinks leads inadvertently to the thought that you yourself can drink with equal impunity. This kind of rationalization is so dangerous that unless the stimulus can be completely and immediately nullified, movies and plays and books portraying drinking must be avoided altogether.

Do not waste time envying people who indulge in alcohol moderately. Alcohol is to some extent physically injurious to everybody, even if there is no outward sign of bodily harm, and those who indulge moderately are generally the first to admit it. To expend your envy on something which so often causes some degree of premature physical, if not mental, deterioration shows a distorted sense of values. Experience has shown that where this foolish attitude existed in the beginning it disappeared when the individual had sufficient opportunity to observe soberly the cumulative effects of alcohol on some of his "moderate" drinking friends.

Avoid undue hurry, which is a result of tenseness but also a cause of it. A person who is fatigued by prolonged unnecessary haste is likely to turn to alcohol to break the resulting condition of tension. If you do not have time for relaxation, try to concentrate on what you are doing, while you are doing it, and on the next thing that you are going to do. Another method of quieting down is to do something with exaggerated precision the moment you discover yourself to be nervous.

One of the most valuable weapons to employ against abnormal drinking is a sense of humor. Excessive drinkers are usually well equipped with this helpful characteristic, only they have not been accustomed to using it on themselves. What could be more ludicrous than a full-grown man's insisting on poisoning himself in a way that brings him little happiness while he is doing it and extreme misery when he tries to stop? Were it not for its tragic ending, this would be comedy on a grand scale. Yet those who can drink only abnormally very seldom see their actions in this light. Use your sense of humor, then, to the full limit, not only at the thought of being so stupid as to drink, but also on contributory character problems such as an ego that seeks satisfaction in a mean or silly manner, or a hypersensitiveness to likes and dislikes which is characteristic of a spoiled child.

Many drinkers resort to alcohol when they are frustrated, upset, or not appreciated by families, employers, or friends. A person with a normal ego and an average disposition, when slighted or unappreciated, will lose his temper. This lets off steam and has the advantage of showing his opponent how he feels. This should clear the air for all concerned, as a thunderstorm gets rid of the heat and humidity of a summer day. This reaction also keeps little resentments from growing into large ones. Resentments, in the long run, only hurt the person who has them and for the alcoholic they are dynamite.

Why the Treatment Takes Time

Alcoholism that has often been many years in the process of formation cannot be permanently removed by a few weeks' effort. It does not take nearly as long to arrest the disease of alcoholism as it took to get it, but it cannot be spirited away by magic in a few days.

No one leads a continuously calm, quiet, and uneventful life. Everybody has a certain amount of worry and sorrow on the one hand, or pleasurable excitement on the other. In order to pass through these unusual emotional situations (as well as through periods of extreme nervous fatigue) without recourse to alcohol as a stabilizer, the ex-drinker needs a reconstructed and stable character. Instead of depending upon whatever reserve stamina he may still possess to fight off these temptations to drink again, his new reaction mechanism should make him think of what happened the last time he drank.

As with any other serious illness, the alcoholic patient must be prepared to carry through a long-term recovery program. He should have regular physical check-ups from a doctor who knows that he is an alcoholic and will take appropriate precautions regarding the use of sedative drugs.

Particularly dangerous periods for an arrested alcoholic are those during recovery from serious illnesses which may have occurred after sobriety. For instance, the sobered alcoholic has sustained a heart attack (other illnesses do happen to people, sober or drunk) and has been confined to the hospital for some time. During the recovery period, or even after the patient has returned to work and normal life, there are noticeable evidences of decreased physical vigor and the resultant necessity of a less active and more precautionary existence. These conditions often bring on depression for the patient, a feeling that youth is gone. This leads to thoughts about lost pleasures, and somehow the subconscious mind brings in the good old days of drinking. These are dangerous thoughts, and misleading as well. The patient may try to prove to himself and others he is still as young as ever, by means of a few drinks "just to raise his spirits" during recovery. This is simple rationalization. If the patient takes time to reflect about such an action, he should realize that it is about the worst thing he could possibly do.

Beyond the Drinking Problem

Never lose sight of the fact that you are learning something that is infinitely more important in the long run than merely ceasing to drink. Sobriety is an essential preliminary, but only a preliminary, to the contented, efficient life that you are seeking. When the inner personality which you have so unsuccessfully tried to escape from in drink is so changed that you no longer need to escape from it, you will be living effectively rather than merely existing in a nervous and depressed state of mind. You will eventually achieve contentment if you will have patience and perseverance.

A complete reorganization of character is bound to take place when the desire for alcohol is removed systematically. This reorganization cannot help having far-reaching effects, more as a result of what is acquired than of what is merely renounced.

Let a frequent survey of your more recent indulgences keep impressing upon you the fact that you have completely exhausted all pleasurable reactions from alcohol. Stop trying to reproduce past experiences. You cannot do it. Neither can you imitate the drinking of your friends who apparently do so without prolonged ill effects. You drank to be happy, and it made you exceedingly unhappy. When you leave alcohol alone you acquire what you futilely sought when you drank—real happiness. Reflect frequently and at length on this paradox of paradoxes.

Meditation

There should be a brief period in everyone's daily life when quiet reflection can take place. This period need not interfere with one's routine affairs. It may be a few minutes of serious thought while traveling to and from work, or while preparing for a night's rest. Some men have said their most constructive thinking about personal affairs has been while shaving in the morning. Perhaps this would correspond to "make-up" time for women. During these few minutes of meditation you may review your personal problems. You may be considering some action which might endanger your sobriety. Quiet meditation may show the proper path: Will this act cause for myself or others more pain than pleasure, if things do not work out as planned? Will my conscience be troubled? After all, one has to live with oneself and regret is an unpleasant load to carry. For the recovering alcoholic particularly, quiet meditation can be very strengthening, even if it is only a minute's thought.

Relaxation and Self-Suggestion

The purpose of relaxation is twofold: first, as an end in itself, which might be called conscious relaxation; second, as a preparation for the suggestion which aims at the re-education of the unconscious mind. The methods of conscious relaxation and self-suggestion described in the following paragraphs may not be immediately understandable to a person who has just stopped drinking; they should be reviewed at a later stage in the recovery process, when they can be more effectively practiced.

The pleasurable effects of alcohol can be divided into two main categories of thought or feeling. One can be designated as will-to-power or self-satisfaction; the second is the feeling of calmness, peace of mind, and poise. The man who has had a drink is afraid of nothing or nobody, at least as far as those fears which are the products of self-consciousness and inferiority feelings are concerned. Furthermore, all petty irritations, unnecessary anxieties, and restlessness disappear—until the effects of the drink begin to wear off. The desire to obtain a feeling of calmness, then, is one of the main reasons for drinking.

The opposite of calmness is mental tension (with its concomitant physical tension), and this tension arises from conflicts within the mind. Frequently the conflicts are caused by—or, at any rate, greatly aggravated by—past drinking and the feelings of inferiority resulting from it, so that the abnormal drinker is caught in a vicious circle which continues to become more vicious with each successive party. For the time being, however, alcohol breaks this mental tension immediately and completely, and this escape from reality through a narcotic and the refusal (through fear of nervous depression) to return to reality lead to continuous drinking. But the relief is very temporary, and in the end alcohol produces a far worse condition than the one it was supposed to cure. If enough alcohol is absorbed in an effort to calm the nerves, delirium tremens will result, and delirium tremens is the quintessence of tension, mental and physical.

Thus if one of the two main stimulations to drink is to be avoided, a constructive method must be found to relieve mental and physical tensions. The nervous individual who has heretofore been attempting to drink away his moods must understand that consciously induced physical relaxation is the solution to this phase of his problem. He must practice it whenever he notices that he is tense. So close is the affiliation of mind and body that a tense mind cannot exist in a thoroughly relaxed body, and when the mind is thoroughly relaxed, no one to whom the problem of abstinence is of prime importance will take a drink.

Incidentally, relaxation provides a new method of facing life, apart from the question of resisting alcohol. The energy saved, the efficiency gained, to say nothing of the peace of mind that results, have often proved to have a definite cash value in the office as well as social value at home. The ability to relax in the face of unexpected difficulties can be an important business asset.

In the creation of a will toward continued sobriety, simple suggestion following deep relaxation has been found genuinely helpful. Although a certain length of time is required for the results to become apparent, the effects are cumulative and permanent. Modern science has proved the existence of the unconscious or subconscious mind and has demonstrated that this part of the mind can be influenced to work in conjunction with the conscious mind. When people are fully conscious, they are straining every idea given them through their critical intelligence, and as a result they confine the question under consideration to their conscious mind. If a person is relaxed, however, and in a somewhat drowsy state, this critical barrier is to some extent removed and the suggested ideas penetrate into the subconscious mind.

One great advantage of relaxation and self-suggestion is that the individual can (and should) treat himself or herself by this method before he goes to sleep at night. The thoughts that we sleep on tend more than any others to shape our feelings and actions. Examples of suggestions to be used as the time for sleep nears are: "Life from now on will be much happier provided I do not take that fatal first drink"; "Another twenty-four hours clear of trouble—Easy does it, on a daily basis, certainly helps"; or any other simple form of assuring oneself that a happy, sober life is preferable to the troubles of the drinking past.

In practicing conscious relaxation and self-suggestion, the following points will prove helpful.

1. If you are sleepy, the conscious relaxation is not necessary, but under no circumstances omit the suggestion about continuance of sobriety, even if it lasts only thirty seconds.

2. Make your pre-sleep suggestion about continued sobriety very simple. Too many ideas or the complicated development of one idea will only wake you up.

3. Do not continue the suggestion to the point of being bored by it. If you are not asleep after three or four minutes, think of non-exciting subjects, then return to the suggestion if you wish.

4. On waking in the morning, start the day with a few minutes of suggestion; relaxation at this time is not necessary.

5. If, during the suggestion, extraneous ideas come to your mind, do not worry about it. Let them disappear without effort, and continue the original train of thought.

6. Do not be disturbed if you cannot relax yourself as well as you can be relaxed by another person. Be content with the knowledge that self-relaxation and self-suggestion are productive enough of constructive mental training to make the practice of them worthwhile.

7. Just as getting into good physical shape requires regular sustained procedure, so the training of the mind and the unconscious mind must be carried on faithfully every day if the desired results are to be obtained.

Maintain a Good Opinion of Yourself

Finally, and most important for your own strength in everyday life, try to avoid actions which will belittle yourself in your own eyes. Any act (entirely apart from drinking) which gives a man a poor opinion of himself has a very direct bearing on his ability to overcome the desire to resume drinking. The minute he recognizes that he has done something incompatible with what he believes to be right, he has feelings of guilt which are dangerous to continued sobriety.

The excesses of the past have given the alcoholic a deep sense of inferiority; therefore every reasonable step must be taken to dispel this depressing idea of self as completely and quickly as possible. Every person has good points and abilities which are noted by his or her associates (mostly without being mentioned). These are often capabilities which others would dearly like to possess. Therefore, why write off these advantages through self-depreciation?

Take stock of your assets. You have them. You have found a way of life which may well be sounder and more constructive than that of many of those around you. Take heart and be dignified in your life of happy sobriety; be good to yourself. You have won a very important contest in life.

∗ 3

THE PERILS OF

CONTROLLED DRINKING

One of the most controversial areas in alcoholism studies is the possibility of a return to "controlled drinking" by those recovering from alcoholism.

There are two major steps in the recovery program of addicted or gamma alcoholics. The first is the establishment of a secure, contented sobriety. No real rehabilitation can take place while alcohol is still present in the system. The second is the building of a new way of life, once the obsession to drink has subsided. This craving, for those suffering from alcoholism, is so enveloping and acute that the sufferer's daily life revolves around obtaining alcohol and the resulting effects on the body, mind, and spirit. This exists for the periodic drinker as well as the daily drinker, since the sober periods between the periodic drinker's binges are still influenced by the past and future consumption of alcohol.

In the words of one leading physician in the field of alcoholism:

It is more effective therapy to substitute one obsession for another—the obsession of being sober for the obsession to get drunk. The obsession to be a controlled drinker means that it would not satisfy the alcoholic any longer merely to be sober. . . . It is therefore of vital concern that he set himself a limit of alcohol and not exceed it. A tremendous amount of his energy and interest is devoted to his recovery in this sense—as against comfortable sobriety which, once achieved, requires less effort.[1]

In a working definition, Dr. Marvin A. Block, formerly Chairman of the American Medical Association Committee on Alcoholism, notes that the principal manifestations of the disease of alcoholism are the "consistently undesirable results following the ingestion of alcohol."[2]

A careful examination of many case histories of alcoholics indicates that during the progression of their illness these people consume alcohol but do not "drink" in the sense that the term is understood by millions of so-called normal drinkers. Drinking is defined according to a well-established procedure. Its practices may vary from country to country, or within one group as compared to another, but, in general, drinking is an activity which, with very few exceptions, occurs always with two or more participants who take pleasure in each other's company. The particular forms of the pleasure felt to be gained, or the unpleasantness felt to be avoided, by this joint participation may be many. It may allow freer conversation, the avoidance of controls not desired in the particular setting, reduction of anxiety, less discriminating and therefore less effortful amusement, forgetting of depressing, irritating or disconcerting matters.

In any group, drinking is a relatively unified custom. Hence controls are provided and behavior approved or disapproved by the same persons whose sanction is important for other behaviors—parents, spouse, members of the social group, and immediate superiors in the job, the lodge, or the club, among others. Readily recognizable as deviations from any of the drinking customs observed in the United States are the behaviors described in the following section, which is abstracted from the article "Alcoholics Do Not Drink" by Selden D. Bacon.[3]

Drinking Behaviors During the Progression
of Alcoholism

1. The individual begins to drink *more* than the other members of his group. If they usually have two or three cocktails, he usually has four or five.

2. The individual begins to drink more frequently than the others. If there are from four to ten occasions a month considered appropriate for drinking and the average group member with the same status as this individual usually activates the custom six to eight times a month, this individual usually imbibes on all ten occasions and probably many other times.

3. The individual shows *more* of that behavior which might be labeled "ordinarily forbidden but given temporary license for socially defined drinking situations." This may mean so-called drunken behavior, but it may only refer to increased noisiness, exhibitionism, carelessness about some proprieties, and so on. This individual with increasing frequency not only reaches to the farthest limit of the allowed license; he often goes beyond. Further, he may define certain situations as being appropriate for this license when others do not.

4. This individual begins to experience "blackouts," temporary amnesias during and following drinking episodes. These are not to be confused with "passing out" or stupor. Such amnesias—certainly their appearance three or more times—do not merely represent differences *in degree* from the other drinkers. They are an accompaniment to the use of alcohol beverages that is not within the limits of *any* drinking custom.

5. The charter of drinking—the usual understandings of members of a given group about why, how often, when, how much, for how long, with whom, what, and so on, of the use of alcohol beverages—becomes inadequate for this individual. He "needs" more and different explanations. He "ra-

tionalizes" his drinking too much and with "excessive" intensity and with bizarre explanations from the point of view of his fellows.

6. He often drinks more rapidly, especially at the start of a drinking situation, than his fellows. He gulps his drink.

7. He begins surreptitious drinking, sneaking drinks, using alcohol in such a fashion that his fellows will not know about it.

8. A crucial behavioral change is called the "loss of control." With increasing frequency the taking of a first drink becomes an effective trigger for the achievement of intoxication. This may occur no matter what the situation. Since only a small percentage of any drinking situations in any subsociety of the area here being discussed allow—to say nothing of calling for—intoxication, the individual at this point becomes rather conspicuous unless strong countermeasures are undertaken.

However, even before such heroic departures from the world of drinking custom are activated, it is extremely doubtful that this individual can still be called a "drinker." To contrast some of these "alcoholic" behaviors with drinking behaviors will serve to underline the conclusion. That aspect of the social function of drinking described as "sociality" or reciprocity of reward (Jones' drinking rewards Smith and vice versa) has not only dwindled, it has gone into reverse. If Jones is our alcoholic, his use of alcohol is with increasing frequency irritating, perhaps frightening, perhaps even measurably damaging to Smith. The various Smiths in the group may even verbalize about this, at first only in joking terms but soon in more serious fashion; they may even leave him out of certain situations. But it is equally clear that the drinking of the "custom-bound" Smiths is not only inadequate but rather irritating to our increasingly alcoholic Mr. Jones. He may "use" the Smiths' cocktail party to get alcohol, but the party itself is of little interest—often, in fact, interferes with his preferred patterns of alcohol consumption.

The functions which alcohol serves for any individual drinker are still gained by Jones. Indeed, they are magnified to the point that most members of his group would call them distorted. The others like drinking. Jones *needs* alcohol.

For the custom of drinking, the time, place, amounts, frequency, involved behaviors, and so on are all covered by rules, most of them fairly readily describable for any given group. Mr. Jones no longer accepts these rules. The charter of drinking is likewise describable. It is not sufficient for Mr. Jones. Mr. Jones has avoided or accepted with no change in his behavior the sanctions brought into play because of his drinking deviations. Mr. Jones has avoided, counterattacked, deceived, or given false promises to the sanctioners of customary drinking.

Other aspects of a custom include its relation to other ways and the importance ascribed to it. Mr. Jones has extended the use of alcohol beverages into times, places, and situations not considered appropriate by his associates. He may take drinks at the office, on the train, or during midday breaks in the work routine or in answer to the mildest headache or cough, although, for the sake of example, let it be said that these situations or other sets of activity are *not* utilized for initiating drinking by his particular associates. And the use of alcohol has become, at the least, one of the most important activities in his total existence.

If there were a gradation of phenomena called psychological, psychopathic, and psychotic and a parallel gradation called social, "sociopathic" and "sociotic," and if the latter could be applied to special areas of behavior, then the individual exhibiting the traits listed so far would, in relation to drinking behavior, be on the borderline between "sociopathic" and "sociotic."

To call him a drinker would be as remote from reality as to call the patient in the dentist chair who receives an alcohol injection a drinker. On the other hand, he still can remind one of a drinker, albeit a distorted reflection with many elements of the usual drinker lacking and with some added attributes quite foreign to the ordinary drinker. And then the picture clearly changes. After a brief intermission of quasi-exploration and quasi-invention, both thinly connected to the world of social drinking, our Mr. Jones usually moves not only to the "sociotic" in relation to alcohol but also to at least the "sociopathic" in other areas of custom. First let us note his quasi-explorations and inventions in relation to drinking.

9. He attempts new patterns of alcohol usage. He switches from bourbon to gin to vodka. He tries "the beer route," perhaps even Rhine wine and soda. He "drinks" only every other day or only after four o'clock. He "drinks" only with his wife or only at home or only away from home, only when eating or when not eating. The variety of activities is fascinating in its individuality and also, paradoxically, in its almost complete similarity to the squirmings and writhings of all the other alcoholics. However, it is not invention in the sociologic meaning of that term. First, the patterns evolved are not supposed to be adopted by anyone else. Second, although others may be fooled as well as Mr. Jones that these are variations from the social usage of drinking, in reality they have little to do with that custom except for the most fragile outer mask; they are merely modes of ingesting alcohol. They are closer to the dentist's injection than to *any* custom of drinking. It is a great pity that wives, friends, even physicians are likely to confuse these activities with drinking.

10. There is another heroic measure open to the alcoholic. He can keep on imbibing in the same fashion, but he can change the social locale. In this way the negative sanctions and sanctioning agents of his group will be eliminated. Mr. Jones can take "the geographic cure." He can move from suburb to central city or from Newark to New Orleans. Failure is built into the adventure before it even starts, but Mr. Jones may travel quite a bit before this becomes obvious. But Mr. Jones can achieve the same results by traveling socially without leaving his own city. He can do his "drinking"

in places and with people who are of a different—almost invariably, from the point of view of his former associates, lower—social status. He can have his alcohol on the other side of the tracks.

This intermediate stage of alcohol-imbibing behavior could at least be said to have pretensions of relationship to social drinking. Actually it is merely a thrashing around by an excited organism in a completely hostile environment. It is more significant for an associated development, one quite distinct from any aspect of alcohol, than it is for the imbibing history of the individual. For now we have to observe two developments in Mr. Jones: he becomes sociotic in relation to drinking; he becomes sociopathic in one or more other areas of custom.

11. Mr. Jones may become a loner. He does his meaningful alcohol injection by himself. This is by definition a complete rejection of drinking.

12. Rather than manifesting excessive rationalizations about alcohol and its use, he avoids any and all discussion of the subject. If forced by physician, friend, minister, wife, employer to consider the matter, he may produce ingenious alibis, outrageous (to common sense) explanations, even barefaced lies. However, he is quite aware of what he is doing, has no personal belief whatever in his statements, is merely trying to stave off, appease, or deceive the custom-bound people who are interfering with him. He is not varying from the social charter. He has denied it.

13. He may start utilizing techniques for the ingestion of alcohol which are beyond the pale of any conceivable development in the drinking usages of his group; starting off the day with seven or eight ounces of gin or whisky; spending four or five days of the ordinary work-a-day week doing nothing but ingesting alcohol; taking alcohol in such forms as mouth-wash, canned heat preparations, vanilla extract, and so on; in addition, he may omit such practices (if they were the norm in his group) as using ice, glasses, chasers, mixes.

14. Concomitant with these last three or four modes of behavior—and often starting much earlier—our hypothetical Mr. Jones has manifested changes, socially unacceptable changes, in areas other than those related to drinking. Dishonesty, excessive rationalization, avoidance, and the other deviations, once perhaps even rare in his behavior, then noticeable where alcohol was concerned, now begin to appear in the family situation or perhaps in friendship groups or on the job. Accidents, job losses, family quarrels, broken friendships, even trouble with the law may take place, not just when he is under the influence of alcohol, but even when he is not. And such occasions quite usually set off further drinking. The social and geographic traveling mentioned earlier may speed this departure from culture and society.

15. Characteristics of the final phases of alcoholism are so exotic, whether concerning drinking or any social behavior, that they need only be mentioned: binges—a complete rejection of social reality; physical tremors, hallucinations, and deliria; horrifying but unidentified fears and hatreds; collapse of all former social status; compulsive hiding and storing of drinks against probable hangovers; surrender of all rationalizations; early death.

Somewhere in this progression, perhaps at about the time of the behaviors numbered 4, 5, and 6, the word drinking no longer applies to this man's use of alcohol. He is no more a drinker than a kleptomaniac is a customer or a pyromaniac is a Camp Fire Girl. Alcoholics may consume alcohol. They do not drink.

Indirectly, members of Alcoholics Anonymous have indicated one proof of this conclusion by a technique they have often suggested to people who were not sure whether or not they were alcoholics. The doubtful one was asked to state what he thought would be a proper social drinking schedule—two cocktails and one highball a day or three highballs or whatever he wished. Then he was told to adhere to that exact schedule, never taking more, never taking less, for twenty-eight days; many felt that ten days would tell the story. The alcoholic could not do it. He could go on the wagon; he could sporadically or steadily get drunk. He could not drink.

The theoretical questions why do they drink so much? why do they drink? why can't they, after therapy, drink again? are now to be seen, not as questions wrongly answered or not yet answered, but as questions containing a false assumption, one that makes any answer impossible. One might as well ask: Why don't worms jump higher?

Applications of the knowledge that alcoholics do not drink might be helpful in a number of situations. There is the wife trying to understand, modify, or explain her alcoholic husband's "drinking." There is the alcoholic worried about his "drinking." There are the physicians and others in the position of therapist or counselor who are worried about their own drinking because it may affect their treatment of the alcoholic's "drinking"; that any physician dealing with a kleptomaniac would worry about his own buying of goods in stores, or when dealing with a pyromaniac, his own habit of lighting cigarettes, is rather doubtful. There is the minister or teacher who, when giving information to the young, may feel that he has to explain drinking in terms of alcoholism and yet is aware that his listeners, especially if their parents are drinkers, will disbelieve everything he says. There are judges who are trying to deal with drinkers who have had "too much" and were a public nuisance or worse as if they were psychologically ill people, and there are other judges dealing actually with alcoholics as if they were rational individuals who would learn "to be better" through punishment, not again let their "drinking" get out of hand.

This is not the first time nor will it be the last that a problem is maintained and enhanced by a confusion between words and reality. In this instance the words alcoholism and drinking have been used as if they were practically the same thing. In fact, one of the great social movements of 1840–1940 in our country (culminating in National Prohibition from 1919 to 1933) carefully nurtured and disseminated the proposition that alcoholism and drinking were one and the same thing. There are connections between drinking and alcoholism: certain drinking customs form an excellent terrain for the emergence of alcoholism; alcohol is a necessary precondition for both; drunkenness is inevitable for one and may occasionally appear in the other. Such connections, however, in no way indicate that the two phenomena are actually one phenomenon. As the preceding description indicates, they are rather strikingly distinct. More widespread appreciation of this fact may help to clarify some of the confusion which still surrounds this extensive, costly, and deeply painful problem of alcoholism.

The drinking behaviors outlined by Professor Bacon are not unusual or extreme cases. During the course of their illness, active alcoholics have experienced many or most of the irrational actions mentioned. After a period of total sobriety, recovering sufferers from the disease usually find that the mind clears, enabling more or less total recall of these former aberrations. Many of the behaviors described are often cited in case histories presented by recovered people—for example, at meetings of Alcoholics Anonymous.

"Controlled Drinking"

In 1962, Dr. D. L. Davies of Maudsley Hospital, London, stated in an article [4] published in the United States that 7 out of 93 patients, followed up from seven to eleven years, had developed the capacity to drink with control; the remaining 86 former patients did not try to re-establish a controlled type of drinking. Dr. Davies' statements aroused much discussion among experts on alcoholism in this country, since the accepted premise in rehabilitating those suffering from alcoholism is based upon the establishment of continued sobriety as the principal means of arresting the disease.

At a meeting of the American Psychiatric Association in 1965, four doctors reported that a follow-up study of 32 male alcoholics who had been discharged as "improved" from the Cincinnati, Ohio, Alcoholism Clinic showed that some alcoholics do manage to return to normal drinking. Of the patients studied, 11 had given up drinking entirely, 10 had backslid and were "pathological" drinkers, and 11 had become "normal" drinkers. The doctors questioned the assumption that abstinence is essential for successful treatment and challenged the belief that no recovered alcoholic can ever again take a drink safely. They stated that the patients "came from our psychiatric court clinic, welfare and social agencies" and that "individual, conjoint and group psychotherapies were provided along with drugs." [5]

Studies of this sort have never included the vast number of gamma-type alcoholics who have progressed into a state of chronic alcoholism from many years of drinking. These are the types—the great majority with homes, families, jobs, and bank accounts—who are drawn from the substantial citizenry of the United States, from all socioeconomic levels, including prosperous executives and their wives. They constitute the majority group of the 400,000 arrested alcoholics who now make up the membership rolls of Alcoholics Anonymous in this country.

Dr. Davies' 1962 report was intended to throw out for discussion among other experts in the field of alcoholism the question: "While among those who treat alcoholics, there is such wide agreement that these patients will never be able to drink 'normally,' might there not be some cases which suggest the contrary and deserve special consideration?" [6]

Dr. Davies seems to have intended to point out in his study, among other more scientific findings, that the exception proves the rule, since in his reply to comments on his article he remarked:

The danger that alcohol addicts under treatment will experiment to see whether they too can drink normally cannot be brushed aside. It should be said that I advised all the patients to aim at lifelong abstinence, and no patient of mine has been encouraged to try to drink normally.

Nor has my practice in this regard changed, and in my article I repeated that "all patients should be told to aim at total abstinence" . . . the patient who challenges the doctor's advice to become a teetotaler, on the basis of what I have reported, should be told that the evidence suggests that only a minority may recover completely, and that he, the patient, would be wiser to assume that he will not be in that group.[7]

The replies to Dr. Davies' article came mainly from authorities in the field of alcoholism in the United States. Practically all agreed that a return to some form of controlled drinking on the part of recovering alcoholics was not only dangerous in the extreme but doomed to failure from the start. Excerpts from some replies follow.

Ruth Fox, M.D., Medical Director of the National Council on Alcoholism:

The article by Dr. D. L. Davies, raising the question of whether or not normal drinking can be resumed by alcoholics, became the basis of an interesting discussion at a conference on Newer Aspects of the Treatment of Alcoholism, convened under the auspices of the National Council on Alcoholism at the New York Academy of Medicine, November 16th and 17th, 1962.

My own practice covers many hundreds of alcoholics, and though I have never been in a position to do a follow-up, I do not know of a single patient of mine who has been able to resume normal drinking. Many of them have tried and failed. There may, of course, have been some who have succeeded in doing this, but if so I do not know about them. Time will have to help answer this problem.[8]

Marvin A. Block, M.D., Chairman 1954–1964, Committee on Alcoholism, American Medical Association:

The cases which Dr. Davies cites are worth reporting, since they point up the possibility that there may be some biochemical changes in some individuals which will allow them to drink eventually, even though they have been diagnosed as alcoholics.

However, this should be thought of as corresponding to the reported spontaneous recoveries in cancer. They are unique, they are different, and they are rare. For the average alcoholic patient to depend upon such a phenomenon, or for the average physician treating alcoholics to hold out to his patients the possibility that they may drink with impunity, would be a disservice to the patients.[9]

Harry N. Tiebout, M.D., psychiatrist, Greenwich, Connecticut:

The statistic that 86 out of 93 [patients of Dr. Davies] did not try to re-establish a controlled type of drinking is also significant. For them, irreversibility is still very real and, I suspect, rightfully so. At least they seem to have no intention of making themselves guinea pigs after seven to eleven years of sobriety.

This attitude characterizes the sober alcoholics with whom I have discussed the Davies article. They express some concern that others may be tempted and they are sorry for those who still are struggling with admitting that control is beyond them.

As for themselves, they place themselves with the 86 and have no desire to return to normal drinking. Unanimously they say that no matter how long they might be drinking normally again, they could never overcome the fear that their control might slip and that they would be plunged once more into the rat-race of their alcoholism. They are comfortable with their sobriety and intend to remain so. They represent, I am sure, the vast majority of sober alcoholics. Davies' material will not distress them.[10]

[Dr. Tiebout, now deceased, was a pioneer in developing the modern approach to alcoholism as an illness. He was also an "early friend" to Alcoholics Anonymous in its beginning years.]

M. M. Glatt, M.D., St. Bernard's Hospital, London, England:

One could speculate about the possibility of an individual threshold—a certain blood alcohol level above which loss of control sets in—the level varying from person to person, and in the same person, depending on a variety of psychological, physical, or psychomatic factors, so that temporarily some alcoholics may be able to control their drinking in the presence of certain "external" (social obligations, etc.) brakes.

Obviously a great deal is still unknown, and much research is necessary, about the loss of control, the varying types of alcoholics, and so on, but as yet treatment of alcoholics should still have as its aim total abstinence.[11]

[Dr. Glatt, one of Europe's foremost authorities on alcoholism, is also known for his chart of alcohol addiction and recovery, now widely used in the United States; see Appendix A.]

Case Histories

The two true case histories which follow are graphic illustrations of the dangers of experimenting with controlled drinking. As in all case histories in this book, the names used are fictitious.

I. A GLASS OR TWO OF WINE

At the time this history begins, Melville Jones, a prominent textile manufacturer, had arrested his alcoholism and enjoyed more than ten years of sobriety.

When the nature of Mr. Jones' illness had become apparent in its more acute phases, his doctor had recommended Alcoholics Anonymous. Previously, like so many others suffering from alcoholism, he had been unable to believe that drinking was the root of his problems. He had consulted psychiatrists, undergone treatment at expensive sanitoriums for "nervous breakdowns," and had been convinced that the pressures of directing his large and successful firm had resulted in various nervous disorders. He had been a drinker of alcoholic beverages since college days and at the time of his joining AA had considered himself a social drinker over a period of thirty years. However, after attending only two or three meetings of the AA group, he recognized the various manifestations of alcoholism and the warning signals described by the group members as applicable to his own case. Accordingly, he stopped drinking at about the same time that he began to be a very active participant in his AA group.

Over the next ten years he was active in many aspects of AA. Then, one spring, he informed his fellow group members that he and his wife were taking a combined business and pleasure trip to Europe for three months. As an elder statesman of ten years standing, respected in his group, he led its closed meeting the night before his departure.

At home the next morning, he remembered his former trips —the marvelous cuisine of the French steamship line, the wines, the relaxed atmosphere. Since joining AA, he had not been to Europe. He had delegated these business-social trips to junior executives, largely because he had never felt strong enough to withstand the temptation of being wined and dined by his European clients. In previous years he had been known to his associates as a connoisseur of vintage wines. The thought occurred to him: "Why not enjoy this trip more fully and relax the entire time? Knowing all the pitfalls of drinking and the warning signals of oncoming trouble, I am certain that I can take a glass or two of wine with meals and stop at that point."

His wife approved the idea, agreeing that he must now have learned when to call a halt. They agreed that he should partake only of wines, with a limit of two glasses once a day during dinner. The three months passed with the agreement kept. Mel thoroughly enjoyed dining with his clients abroad and again selecting the proper wines for special dinners. He never drank anything stronger than table wines (within the limit of two glasses) and only as an accompaniment to food at evening dinner.

On his return, he suggested having a glass or two of mild wine on certain occasions at home. His wife, however, pointed out that he could not honestly return to AA meetings unless he returned to complete sobriety. He realized the justice of her remarks and never mentioned the subject again. But, in his own mind, he rebelled. He rationalized, "I'm not getting any younger [he was sixty-one]. Why should I miss a simple pleasure while I am able to enjoy it?"

So, now feeling some self-pity, he began to stop in a bar near his office on the way home each evening and take one and sometimes two drinks—but never more—of Dubonnet. He selected Dubonnet as less potent than many other wines and thus salved his conscience. Also he chose the business neighborhood bar because he knew none of the other customers and thus word would not reach his wife.

He did, however, feel guilt from time to time; he realized that he was being dishonest. So he decided to drop his attendance at AA meetings at least for the time being. To explain his absence, he informed the presiding chairman of his AA group that a series of business meetings had been scheduled for the next few months on the same night of the week as the AA meetings. He told his wife that he was skipping the AA meetings for a while in order to do some serious reading. In the end, he felt so self-righteous about the whole situation that he sometimes drank sherry or had a third glass of Dubonnet, just to celebrate his cleverness in obtaining a few minutes of "simple" pleasure.

On New Year's Day Mel attended the annual open house at his club with his wife. On these occasions the club served a special New Year's punch, containing brandy, rum, lemon juice, white wine, and sparkling water, with sugar and seasonings. It was ladled from the club's silver punch bowl into special silver goblets. A New Year's Day dinner followed. Almost automatically Mel took a goblet of punch. It proved a stronger potion than he had counted on, and his sobriety pattern had already been broken. With only two drinks of the punch, the old obsession returned.

After dinner he took his wife home, made an excuse for going out, and returned to the club, where he immediately joined a group at the bar and had several brandies.

Within a matter of days he was again drinking just as he had done ten years earlier. This went on for six months, with the obsession to drink much more pronounced than it had been before the sober period. Finally the drinking grew so evident that his wife became alarmed. By this time he was keeping a bottle of liquor in his desk, something he had never done before; drinking at lunch, either alone or with guests; stopping in at a bar on the way home at night. Unable to disguise the fact that he was once more a full-time drinker, he insisted on cocktails before dinner and ended the evening with highballs. He often went to bed drunk and could not remember many parts of the day's activities.

At the end of the six months, he was hospitalized for chronic alcoholism. Prior to that he had appeared at his office in an intoxicated condition, and once a junior member of the firm had been delegated to take him home to prevent his condition's becoming apparent to the staff. Finally he collapsed at home, had an alcoholic convulsion before a doctor could be summoned, and had to be taken to the hospital by ambulance.

While recovering, Melville Jones was visited by several members of his former AA group. His wife had told them why he had failed to attend meetings during the past six months. He was at first loath to see them, feeling that as an elder statesman in the group he had been a conspicuous failure. His guilt and remorse might easily have resulted in a resumption of drinking upon discharge from the hospital. However, the understanding of his AA associates helped him realize that his failure had only resulted from the mistaken belief that after ten years' sobriety he could drink moderately again.

To restore his health and shattered nerves, he agreed to go from the hospital to an AA-sponsored rest home in the country where he spent six weeks. On returning, he rejoined his AA group and was treated as though nothing had happened. Today he is in his fourth year of new sobriety. His case history is reported here as he recounted it at open AA meetings.

This case history was submitted to a selected group of arrested alcoholics, people whose experience with the problem extends far beyond their own individual cases. A digest of their comments follows:

Mr. J. was in trouble with his first glass of wine on the boat. His knowledge of alcoholism should have made him realize this fact. He broke the pattern of his long-term sobriety which had been his chief bulwark.

He allowed his subconscious urge to drink to come to his conscious thinking, after this desire had been compelled to lie latent for years through his vigorous determination to maintain sobriety.

He became overconfident about his own reactions to alcohol. A decade of non-drinking had made him complacent since he had let himself forget the serious trouble of his drinking days.

He had overlooked the constant need of reaffirmation of his resolves for sobriety, since for a long time he had not even toyed with the idea of taking a drink. When the thought occurred at the crucial moment, on the morning of his departure, his almost automatic refusal in the past to consider such a thought seriously did not come to the fore this time.

In his subconscious mind, he was really getting ready to drink again. Consciously, until he actually did take the first glass of wine, he had so rationalized the whole experiment that it almost seemed adventurous and a non-harmful act to prove his own strength.

By "nibbling" upon returning home, after getting through what he considered a successful experiment, he was really in trouble because:

1. He had stopped the therapy of AA meetings.
2. He had lied to his wife and to others.

3. He had "hidden" his drinking by frequenting a strange background.

Therefore when the fatal drink or two of the New Year's punch was taken, he was a "sitting duck." The higher content of alcohol sent him down the path toward the obsession to drink and uncontrolled drinking, faster than the lighter wine libations had done.

But even had he continued on the wine schedule, he was destined for trouble. He had even increased this schedule from one to two glasses to more on certain occasions. It was only a matter of more time until he would have been in difficulty.

II. "DRINKING IS NOT MY PROBLEM"

Mrs. Alice Lowe was a defiant and confused person when she appeared for an initial appointment in a psychiatrist's office in her Connecticut town. Only two weeks before her husband had won a divorce in the Connecticut courts, which included custody of their two young children. He had charged her with chronic alcoholism. [A condition of "habitual intemperance," if proven, constitutes legal grounds for divorce in Connecticut.] The notoriety of the terms of divorce (carried in the local newspapers), the stigma still attached to alcoholism, especially that of a woman, her intense feeling of rejection by her family and others all combined with the shock of the adverse court decision to place her in an agitated and highly nervous state. Recent heavy drinking had not helped.

Alice Lowe did not believe she had a drinking problem. She had bitterly protested at the trial that her husband was simply using this pretext to get rid of her because of his interest in another woman (not named). However, testimony introduced in behalf of the husband had seemed to prove otherwise: her arrest the previous year for drunken driving; a recent scene in her surgeon husband's office in an intoxicated condition; repeated late-night telephone calls to neighbors and friends in which she used insulting language.

Yet Alice firmly maintained that her drinking was not the cause of her family difficulties—it was rather the cruel behavior of her spouse, his estrangement of the children from her control as a mother, the slanderous gossip of her neighbors and "so-called friends." As she often pointed out, she had been a social drinker for many years before these recent troubles and no one had considered her behavior anything but proper and conventional.

She told Dr. Thompson, the psychiatrist, at her first appointment that her visit had been prompted by her need for professional help in this time of severe mental depression. At times recently, she said, she had been subject to uncontrollable hysteria; she did not mention that she had been drinking heavily since the divorce trial.

Alice Lowe was fortunate in her choice of a doctor. Dr. Thompson, besides his skill in dealing with many other physical and mental disorders, was also an authority on the complexities of alcoholism as an illness. Alice was not aware of his reputation in this respect.

Nor did Dr. Thompson at first mention drinking. After two lengthy consultations in his office, he prevailed upon her to go into the local hospital for certain physical tests. Actually he strongly suspected alcoholism as the basis of all her recent troubles and had also found that she suffered from malnutrition and was near a nervous collapse. He now wished to note her withdrawal symptoms during a period in which liquor would be unavailable.

The hospital stay was beneficial for Alice's physical and mental condition. Vitamin shots, the relaxation of her nerves through properly administered sedatives and tranquilizers, sound sleep, and the return of an appetite for nourishing food all combined to create a sense of partial well-being.

On her first visit after release from the hospital, Dr. Thompson told her frankly that he considered her an alcoholic and, unless she stopped drinking entirely, he could not do much to help her.

For once, Alice Lowe was honest. "But how can I do this, Doctor? I have tried to stop drinking several times and have always failed in the end."

"You cannot do it alone, Mrs. Lowe," replied Dr. Thompson. "You will need help. Alcoholism is a disease which transcends will power, character, or determination."

"Well, where can I get this help?"

Dr. Thompson recommended Alcoholics Anonymous and told her he could arrange for a member of the local group to take her to a meeting. But Alice stated emphatically that she would have nothing to do with AA. She told Dr. Thompson that her embarrassment and sorrow over her separation from her children, her shame at the unfavorable publicity of the divorce, her notoriety among the residents of her home town, all combined to make her avoid any public appearances. "No," she said, "AA meetings are out. What other means of coping with this so-called alcoholism of mine can be tried?"

"There are other ways," the doctor told her. "Would you be willing to place yourself in a course of treatment which will require complete honesty, sincerity, and some humility? In other words, faithfully carry out all my recommendations and tell me honestly your reactions to this new way of life? Such a general approach has worked for others in your situation."

Fearful that the doctor would drop her case, Alice agreed to attempt to carry out the new recommendations. The doctor wrote a prescription for Antabuse.

"As you may suspect, you are not allowed to drink any alcoholic beverage during this treatment, not even wine or beer. For the first two weeks take a whole Antabuse pill on arising each morning. Thereafter half a pill will be sufficient. You must realize that if you drink you will be seriously ill shortly thereafter. Taking this Antabuse pill every day is a reaffirmation you do not want to drink that day. If you stop taking these pills, it means you want to drink again."

He also advised Alice to move out of her former home. Her many years of living there as a wife and mother had left too many remembrances of the past, which created morbidity and self-pity. She put the house up for sale and took a small apartment in the village. Dr. Thompson then made an appointment for her with the director of an out-patient clinic for alcoholism operated by the state of Connecticut in a nearby larger town. After the interview, she enrolled in twice-weekly group therapy classes on alcoholism.

Dr. Thompson suggested that she get a part-time job rather than remain idle, a prey to feelings of loneliness and rejection. Alice, who had some financial means of her own and a small court-granted alimony, pointed out that she had no business experience and would have to be a clerk or sales person. This again would require her facing the public, which she dreaded.

The doctor knew from her records that as a young woman she had been a practicing Registered Nurse on the staff of a big New York hospital. (It was there that she had met her former husband.) Dr. Thompson suggested that she become a volunteer aid at the local hospital, which he could arrange. In this way, he pointed out, she would be doing things for others and could get outside herself and forget her own problems for a few hours daily.

With her group therapy classes, new living quarters, a part-time volunteer job which required attendance five days a week, a schedule of "staying away from the first drink each twenty-four hours," and frequent consultations with Dr. Thompson aimed at reducing the guilt feelings and general nervous tension caused by her former drinking, Alice Lowe entered a new way of life. She followed directions honestly and completely, as Dr. Thompson had impressed upon her she must do if this undertaking were to succeed.

Although the first few months were difficult, she carried out all the suggested procedures. She arranged her hours at the hospital so that she worked until the dinner hour, in order to be occupied during what had been the cocktail period in her old way of life. She employed a maid to come in late in the afternoon, so that dinner would be ready on her return from the hospital. Dr. Thompson had prescribed a high-protein diet which also included rich desserts to help quell the desire for alcohol after eating. Her daily tasks left her physically tired and she was usually in bed by 10 o'clock. On weekends, upon her doctor's advice, she began playing golf again, as in years past, but she chose a municipal course in a nearby town where she was not likely to encounter friends of her former husband or former acquaintances.

By the time six months had passed, Alice Lowe felt mentally and physically rejuvenated. This was apparent not only to herself but to Dr. Thompson as well. In fact she was once again an attractive person. In her regular weekly (later semi-monthly) visits at the doctor's office her recovery from the ravages of alcoholism was evident. She appeared to have faced up to herself and life in general. However, there was one discordant note: she was still not thoroughly convinced that drinking had been the primary cause of her past troubles. Although she rigorously maintained sobriety and followed the doctor's directions faithfully, her motivation came from the urge to "show them all" that she was *not* an alcoholic. At times the thought recurred: "Some day I'll be able to drink again, in moderation and like a lady."

When Alice mentioned such a possibility to Dr. Thompson some months after her new life had demonstrated signs of stability, he said to her thoughtfully, "Are not things much better for you now than when you first came to see me? You must accept the plain fact that, for you, alcohol is a poison. My whole plan of treatment rests on this premise. I had hoped that, as health and calmness came back to you, you would totally accept the fact that you can never drink again without re-activating your illness. Actually you are fortunate; many people do not recover. You have complied with treatment; now let's see some acceptance of your true condition. After all, diabetics cannot eat chocolate cake—you cannot drink alcohol. Is this anything to be ashamed of?"

At the time Alice recognized the doctor's logic. As time passed, however, the old doubts returned. "Perhaps some day I'll show them all how wrong they were!"

It was at the hospital that she met Dr. Morgan, a man of about her own age, and they began having luncheon together in the hospital cafeteria. She learned that he was unmarried, had only recently joined the local hospital staff, came from a nearby large city, where he had not only established a practice as a pediatrician but also served as a consultant on the staff of one of the largest hospitals in that city. When she asked him why he had given up this career to come to a small town, he replied that he preferred to live in the country.

One evening she invited him to her apartment for dinner with two of her golfing friends. He remained after the others had gone and they chatted for a while. Suddenly he said, "You know, some of the other people on the hospital staff have told me about you. They admire you for the way you have straightened out your life and stopped drinking. How did you do it?"

Alice had not received a compliment in so long that the thought of other people's speaking kindly about her almost brought her to tears. She told Dr. Morgan her whole history, stressing the wonderful medical care Dr. Thompson had given her.

When she had finished Dr. Morgan was silent for some time. She finally remarked, "You seem very quiet." He replied, "Well, I don't know how to tell you and I am reluctant to bring my personal problems to someone who is now courageously facing her own." She urged him to do so, if she could be of any help, and he continued, "The real reason I am now in this Connecticut town instead of the city where I used to live and work is alcohol. I too have a drinking problem."

"You! I can't believe it!" she replied.

He went on to tell her all about his difficulty with alcohol. As his troubles with drinking increased to the point where he could no longer maintain his appointments with patients and only with difficulty was able to present a sober appearance on his hospital duties, he had become terrified that he would be recognized as an active alcoholic by his colleagues and patients. In desperation he had severed all ties in the city and come to an area where he had hoped that rural surroundings and new associations would perhaps enable him to cut down on his more or less secret drinking.

Alice Lowe was astounded—first, that someone else had the same drinking problem; second, because she had believed that professional people did not succumb to such personal failings. She offered Dr. Morgan her help, suggested that she arrange an appointment with Dr. Thompson as soon as possible, assured him she would keep their conversation entirely confidential.

When Dr. Thompson heard the story, he was pleased for Mrs. Lowe's sake. "This will now give you the opportunity to be of help to another alcoholic. It will be good for both of you."

Now Alice Lowe had a novice to train in keeping away from the first drink. Their mutual interest brought them together frequently. She was a good teacher and he quickly adjusted to a program of life without alcohol. Both of them now had an interest outside of themselves, for while Alice was interested in helping Dr. Morgan to maintain sobriety, the doctor became interested in Alice. Within six months they were married.

The new Mrs. Morgan was completely "respectable" again, she happily thought to herself at times. She was married to an attractive professional man and had a new house of her own. After a short time, she petitioned the Court for a relaxing of her terms of divorce, and through the testimony of many friends was allowed to see her children every other week for a full weekend in her new home.

Dr. Morgan, with Alice's help, had gained complete sobriety. He continued his consultations with Dr. Thompson, attended with Alice the twice-weekly group therapy sessions, and worked with other patients of Dr. Thompson's who were troubled with drinking problems. Even after a year's complete sobriety, he continued to take an Antabuse pill daily. One day, he explained his tardiness for dinner: "I ran out of Antabuse this morning and after work I drove into town for a re-fill."

Alice chided him for his haste in securing a new supply. "One would think you might start drinking right away without that daily pill. My heavens, you have been sober for a year."

"Agreed," said Dr. Morgan "but my work with other alcoholics and my group therapy classes are my money in the bank against drinking. These Antabuse pills are my insurance against a sudden impulse."

Alice pointed out that, with Dr. Thompson's reluctant permission, she had stopped Antabuse after her first six months of treatment. "I have been sober a long time since!"

Within a couple of years Mrs. Morgan had regained the love of her children, had a devoted husband, and was happier than she had ever been in her life. She had been living a life of complete sobriety for six years. But she had departed from the regimen prescribed by Dr. Thompson. As renewed community life occupied her, she dropped her group therapy classes. Her husband continued these meetings and had recently been appointed one of the physicians on the Advisory Board of the State Alcoholism Commission. In addition to discontinuing Antabuse, Alice had convinced Dr. Thompson that a monthly visit to him would be sufficient for her welfare. For a time, she had continued her volunteer work on a curtailed schedule but had given it up within a year after her marriage.

Social life, committee meetings, club memberships, charity benefits brought Alice slowly back to the pattern of her old life with her former husband. Subconsciously, this was a sort of revenge for her. She secretly delighted in having former friends and acquaintances seek her out, compliment her on her appearance, invite her to their homes. "I'm showing them how wrong they were about me," she thought.

The whole subject of problem drinking, or alcoholism as an illness, became distasteful to Alice. When queried about her refusal of alcoholic beverages by new friends or those who had known her before her drinking days, she would reply, "Oh, some people thought I had a drinking problem. I never did; I just decided to stop drinking anyway."

Alice and Dr. Morgan had agreed early in their married life that cocktails could be served to guests in their home without danger to themselves. They drank non-alcoholic beverages. Alice had her initial drink at a neighbor's house, before a charity committee meeting. The neighbor had appeared as a witness for Alice's former husband at the divorce trial. She had asked Alice to come early as she wanted to talk privately about something which had been on her mind for some years. She told Alice, "I have owed you an apology for a long time. I sincerely thought you were addicted to drink when Dr. Lowe asked me to testify. I was wrong and I am truly sorry." She added, "Let's have a cocktail in celebration of our new friendship."

Alice sipped the cocktail but took no more then, nor for a month thereafter. Then one evening, just before dinner, she received a phone call which upset her. Her daughter had fallen from a pony and suffered a concussion. She turned to her husband and said, "I need a drink and I'm going to have just one before I rush to the hospital." He said nothing. The child recovered, but Alice continued to have one drink before dinner. Outside her home, when her husband was not with her, she had a limit of two cocktails, and sometimes she had two cocktails at home when guests were present.

Four months after her first drink, Alice was exceeding her two-drink limit, both at home and outside. Her husband begged her in vain to return to Dr. Thompson, a connection she had severed soon after her resumption of "moderate" drinking. Dr. Morgan also asked Alice to give up all community activities, return with him to group therapy classes, go back to Antabuse. She refused, adding, "You now must understand I was not, and am not now, an alcoholic. I can control my social drinking, just like the majority of people."

To say that her husband was apprehensive and worried is an understatement. Within a month his fears were justified. Alice was arrested for drunken driving and jailed in a nearby town where she had attended a garden club exhibit, followed by a cocktail party. Her husband got her released on bail and secured a noted lawyer to defend her, but the court ruled against her and her driving license was suspended for a year.

Within the next month she resumed drinking in the same pattern which had wrecked her first marriage. Finally, Dr. Morgan had to have her committed to a sanitorium for acute alcoholism. Upon her release, on the insistence of her husband, she went to see Dr. Thompson. But this time he sensed that she had not returned humbly to admit her weakness and ask for help, as she had done originally. Her egoism and defiance were noticeable. Although she lied to him about her liquor consumption, Dr. Thompson clearly understood her condition and pleaded with her to start anew in the regimen of sobriety she had successfully pursued for six years. She half-heartedly agreed, was late for the next appointment, had clearly been drinking, and never returned to his office.

By now she was laden with guilt feelings. She withdrew from all social contacts, began to hide her alcohol supply about the house and garage, and was often "dead drunk" upon her husband's return in the evening.

He finally issued an ultimatum. "You are ruining both yourself and my professional reputation. You will either return to a life of complete sobriety or I must ask for a legal separation."

She refused and was unconscious from alcohol when he returned home in the evening. By this time, her first husband had ceased to allow the children to visit her. Her drinking was now widely known in the community. She had often been seen noticeably intoxicated, on the streets and in various shopping areas. Dr. Morgan kept postponing leaving her. Twice he brought Dr. Thompson to the house, but Alice refused to see him.

On an evening just before Christmas she was not in the living room when her husband came home. He called upstairs; there was no answer. That afternoon she had given the cook and maid the afternoon off with money to go Christmas shopping. There seemed to be no one in the house. After a time her husband became apprehensive and went upstairs to their bedroom. He found Alice on the floor unconscious, with a half-empty bottle of

Bourbon and an empty bottle of barbiturate tablets nearby. She died that night without regaining consciousness. The autopsy showed that death was occasioned by the combination of alcohol and barbiturates. Her grief-stricken husband telephoned Dr. Lowe, and with the two children they attended the funeral in a local church on the afternoon of Christmas Eve. Aside from some former co-workers at the hospital, few others were there. The "friends" she had tried so hard to impress were absent.

This case history was submitted to the same group that reviewed the preceding one. A digest of their comments follows:

> Mrs. Morgan never wholly accepted her condition of alcoholism. For a long time she had complied with a program which brought her six years of sobriety. Subconsciously she had never accepted the fact that she suffered from a disease which precluded her ever drinking again.
>
> Comfortable or happy sobriety never became for her the desired way of life.
>
> Alice was enabled to stay sober, first through daily Antabuse, secondly, through getting outside of herself in working to help others (as a volunteer at the hospital). Her attendance at the group therapy classes kept reminding her of drinking as her basic problem.
>
> After her marriage, slowly but surely, she dropped all her safeguards. Her interests were turned from concern for her sobriety and hospital work, which involved helping others, to the sort of self-absorbed life which had brought her to Dr. Thompson in the first place, for social drinking seemed an integral part of this social life to Mrs. Morgan.
>
> This behavior was in marked contrast to her second husband's not only in his being able to grasp the seriousness of alcoholism as a disease, but also in his determination to safeguard his own sobriety. He had *accepted* the fact that he suffered from a complex and dangerous illness. His concern was not to re-activate its progression. Through constant work

with others, outside his own professional practice, he constantly reminded himself of the fact that sobriety was, for him, the sensible and necessary way of life.

Alice Morgan had never gained confidence in herself to do what was right, irrespective of others' opinions. Like many sufferers from alcoholism, her judgments were often immature and her dependence upon other people's good will—and even their flattery—was a tragic flaw in her character.

Psychologists say that Mrs. Morgan had really been preparing to drink for a long time before she actually did so, whether her conscious mind knew it or not. Subconsciously she had often rationalized, "Some day I'll show them I can drink socially and like a lady," and consciously she had then been motivated to drop her safeguards, one by one.

Both professional people and those safely recovered from alcoholism agree that the crucial points were:

1. Breaking the pattern of a six-year sobriety in a moment of impulsive reaction to flattery and, in certain respects, revenge. This was really the moment of demonstration in controlled drinking that Alice Morgan had long awaited.

2. Taking a drink when she was frightened by her child's accident. Having broken the pattern she was open to temptation the second time.

3. Her non-recognition of danger when she found it was impossible to keep her steadily increasing drinking within the limits she had set in the beginning. This was actually the point of no return, when danger signals should have convinced her of the crucial necessity of seeking help once more from those who had helped her maintain her sobriety in the past—her doctor, her husband, and her clinic director.

From this point on Alice Morgan never had a chance to retrace her steps; the progression of the disease, the obsession for alcohol created by this progression, and her trust in controlled drinking—all combined to distort what little judgment and sense of survival remained.

* 4

SOME PHYSIOLOGICAL APPROACHES

The gamma alcoholic has been described as showing a definite progression from psychological to physical dependence. In other words, the sick person's abnormal reaction to the effects of alcohol progresses from mental preoccupation with drinking to an actual physical dependency on alcohol. Yet the physiological features of the disease have been to some extent neglected by scientists examining the total picture of the illness. Instead, cultural and social-psychological causes and symptoms have been emphasized. In October 1964 the Smithers Foundation, in conjunction with the Clayton Foundation Biochemical Institute of the University of Texas, convened a symposium of the biochemical and nutritional aspects of alcoholism. The speeches and discussions constituted an important contribution to the understanding of the disease of alcoholism. Three of these speeches, selected because they are not too technical for the interested layman, are included here in slightly condensed form.[1] (For a complete report of the symposium, see Selected Reading List.)

Fundamental Considerations Relating Alcoholism to Biochemistry and Nutrition

[*Address by Roger J. Williams, Ph.D., D.Sc., Department of Chemistry and Clayton Foundation Biochemical Institute, University of Texas*]

Faced as we are with a malady for which there is no generally recognized treatment and no generally recognized etiology, a serious attack by those whose thinking is oriented biochemically is past due. There is reason for optimism about the end result because of a profound and rapidly growing belief, based upon an enormous accumulation of evidence, that biochemical considerations hold the key to advance with respect to most maladies which have not yet yielded to medical science. This view is heartily endorsed even by many leaders in medicine who have scarcely more than a nodding acquaintance with the details of modern biochemistry and have no vested interest in the area. . . .

Some biochemical facts that seem highly pertinent should be discussed first.

Fact No. 1. Every human being is, in terms of his biochemistry, innately highly distinctive. Sir A. E. Garrod in 1902 in connection with his study of "inborn errors of metabolism" was the first to recognize the probability "that just as no two individuals of a species are absolutely identical in bodily structure, neither are their chemical processes carried out on exactly the same lines." Subsequent studies, principally during the last decade, have not only confirmed this probability but have revealed numerous and often large biochemical differences between so-called normal individuals.

The evidence for this striking individuality is both indirect and direct. Advances in the realm of biochemical genetics make inevitable the existence of a distinctive pattern of metabolism for every individual, because each individual has a distinctive inheritance and the enzymes which govern the biochemical workings of our bodies are unquestionably linked with genes.

This distinctiveness, in so far as it exists, seems pertinent to the problem of alcoholism, because alcoholism is manifestly a disease to which some individuals are prone while others show no such leaning whatever. Alcoholism is not a disease which attacks whole families, whole communities, or whole countries; it attacks only certain individuals.

Are individual biochemistries sufficiently different from one another so that differences in susceptibility can be ac-

counted for on this basis? Let us look briefly into the nature
and magnitude of the inter-individual differences; these can
only be found by direct observation and experiment. Abun-
dant evidence on this subject—often difficult to believe and
mostly discovered inadvertently—has been collected in my
book *Biochemical Individuality*.[2]

These biochemical differences include compositional
differences (with respect to both inorganic and organic
components) in blood, urine, saliva, digestive juices, bone,
and every other tissue that has been investigated. These
differences are often several-fold in magnitude. Enzyme activities have been investigated predominantly in the blood and
have been found to be highly distinctive for each individual
in accordance with the predictions based upon the fundamental findings of biochemical genetics. Inter-individual variations of specific enzyme levels of two- to five-fold or more
have been observed.

Each individual's endocrine system is highly distinctive
as determined by blood hormone levels (when measurable)
or by anatomical differences between so-called "normal"
glands. Five-fold variations among "normal" individuals often
exist with respect to individual items.

Pharmacological responses, especially when studied both
qualitatively and quantitatively, are likewise highly individual. This would be expected in the light of the other facts.
Individual chemical agents, such as drugs, may yield many
different side reactions or none at all, depending on the
individual receiving them. The dosage required in different
individuals may differ ten-fold or even more. Alcohol is not
exceptional in this regard. All narcotic and other drugs yield
strikingly different results qualitatively and quantitatively
when administered in the same way to a series of individuals.

Growth patterns differ substantially from individual to
individual; so do temperature-control mechanisms, and reactions to anoxia, to electricity, to infective agents, and to
allergens.

The findings of biochemical genetics lead to the prediction that there will inevitably be differences in nutritional needs because of differences in the inherited metabolic machinery. These predictions are amply borne out with respect to minerals, amino acids, and vitamins. In some cases fivefold variations in specific human needs have been established; in other cases the variations are not as wide as this, though they may still be highly significant. In the case of some nutrients which have not been adequately investigated the variations may be much wider.

The fact of biochemical individuality is one that merits emphasis in any biochemical approach to the subject of alcoholism. One of the obstacles in the way of its easy application is the undeniable fact that no individual maintains perfectly constant compositional values, enzyme levels, endocrine activities, and so forth. In other words, there is also intra-individual variation which must be taken into account. The fact of intra-individual variation should not blind us, though it often appears to, to the innate individuality each of us possesses. If anyone doubts the existence of this striking individuality, I suggest that he put it to a test: select any two similar representative members of the human family for careful biochemical comparison. Such a comparison will be convincing.

Fact No. 2. There is, throughout nature, a high degree of biochemical unity. In spite of the enormous amount of detailed metabolic diversity which exists, the very same amino acids, minerals, sugars, and vitamins are used in the metabolic machinery of all kinds of living things from microscopic bacteria to whales. If the metabolic machinery in an earthworm or insect did not involve the very same substances that are involved in the metabolic apparatus of a robin, the mother robin would kill its young by feeding it an insect or worm. If an insect did not possess the same elements in its metabolic machinery as a green plant, the green carnivorous plant would gain no nourishment but would only suffer damage by trapping an insect.

This fact of biochemical unity with respect to metabolic machinery and its operation places all types of experiments involving other organisms than man in an entirely new perspective.

Fact No. 3. Through the mediation of hormones and neurohormones, emotional or psychological stresses can substantially alter one's body chemistry. Psychological factors should not be thought of as completely distinct and independent of biochemistry, but as intimately tied to it. Biochemical change resulting from psychological suggestion has been demonstrated so often that the fact is not subject to debate.

Fact No. 4. In order to maintain their health and activity, our body cells must be furnished water, oxygen, and necessary nutrients from their environment. If any necessary nutrient is withheld or is in short supply, the cells are impaired. This impairment can be slight or serious, because cells can be nourished at many levels of efficiency, as has been amply shown by biochemical tissue culture studies.

Fact No. 5. Each type of body cell may have its own distinctive nutritional needs. Tissue culture studies have demonstrated this. In addition, because of the biochemical individuality residing in each of us, we must deduce that the cells in one individual's body do not have, in the quantitative sense, exactly the same nutritional needs as the corresponding cells in another's body.

Fact No. 6. Whenever a chemical agent has a pharmacological or physiological effect, there is an interaction between the agent and the cells affected. Each type of cell and tissue may be affected differently because of its distinctive composition and metabolic function. This fact leads us to conclude that the whole story of the effects of alcohol cannot be learned by finding out more and more about alcohol. We must think in terms of the biochemical interactions between alcohol and living systems, which are exceedingly complex.

In addition to these facts there is a basic general assumption with which most of those with a biochemical background would probably start: *Whenever a disorder exists in the body, impairment of cellular functions is somehow involved.* It is hard for one who is biochemically oriented to imagine any diseased condition existing in a body in which the metabolism of every cell and tissue is in perfect working order and functioning in accordance with the needs of the organism. A biochemically oriented investigator would be inclined to accept this general assumption axiomatically with respect to every disease and to inquire with respect to alcoholism, as with respect to all other diseases: "What specific cells and tissues are impaired, and how?"

Using as a basis the six facts and the one general assumption, I have during the past fifteen years developed some ideas about alcoholism. It is not expected that these ideas will be accepted uncritically by anyone; it is hoped that they will be weighed and found at least to be stimulative. Up to now this discussion has considered certain facts and one basic assumption which many will find useful and acceptable. We shall now be dealing with probabilities.

To the question: "What cells and tissues are primarily impaired in alcoholism?" the most probable answer seems to be: those cells and tissues having to do with the regulation of appetites—general and specific.

The one common denominator of all alcoholics, whether rich or poor, religious or irreligious, extroverts or introverts, repulsive or charming, dominant or submissive, brilliant or dull, with or without family troubles, emotionally disturbed or otherwise, is their exaggerated desire to ingest alcohol. They often are poor eaters and when the diseased condition becomes advanced they not only have the crucial desire for alcohol but often exhibit in addition an extreme aversion to food, showing plainly that there is serious impairment of the appetite mechanisms.

These mechanisms are themselves complex and not well understood; many are doubtless affected by complex hormonal influences. It is not known how specific these mechanisms are; there is no necessity to suppose that there are separate cells and tissues operative in connection with each chemical substance which may be ingested, yet there are physiological and biochemical mechanisms of a somewhat specific nature which govern the consumption of food in general, of water, and of specific nutrients like salt, calcium, phosphate, certain B vitamins, fat, and sugar. Impairment of these mechanisms has been observed clinically and can often be induced experimentally in animals. Diabetics, it is well known, often have an intense craving for sugar, though physiologically their mechanism for handling it is seriously impaired.

In extreme alcoholism many cells and tissues in the body are adversely affected. Liver damage, for example, is common, and its relation to the disease alcoholism needs to be further clarified. This damage seems to be a result of alcoholism and not its antecedent. It is not observed in early alcoholics and it may be found in those who drink heavily but do not exhibit the more typical symptoms of a compulsive drinker.

The appetite-controlling cells and tissues, then, are probably the ones primarily affected in alcoholism; the other cell damages are probably secondary.

If we accept this probability, the next question is: "How are these cells and tissues impaired?" Before attempting to answer this, it will be well to outline briefly what cells in general need and what can possibly go wrong with them.

The known requirements of cells include (1) water, (2) oxygen, (3) a suitable ambient temperature, (4) about forty different nutrients (minerals, amino acids, vitamins), and (5) freedom from poisons and damaging radiations. In addition, there are other hormonal and regulatory factors which must keep cells functioning properly within the framework of the whole organism. About these relatively little is known. If any one of the cellular needs, including each of the nutrients, is not supplied adequately, cellular health is impaired. To answer the question: "How are the appetite-controlling cells and tissues impaired?" we may say with considerable assurance that the primary factor is alcohol, which is, in sufficient concentration, a poison. If alcohol did not exist there would obviously be no alcoholism.

But alcohol has many different toxic effects. It may cause incoordinated movements, lack of balance, slurred speech, vomiting, double vision, weeping, laughing, fighting, sleepiness, and so on. These responses are highly variable from individual to individual. In some rare individuals a relatively small amount of alcohol may cause them to go berserk. None of these effects, however, is alcoholism. Alcohol has in addition another toxic effect; it can induce, *in some individuals*, a seemingly uncontrollable desire to drink more alcohol. This seems to be the alcoholism effect, and therefore the crux of the problem. If alcohol had all its other toxic effects and lacked the ability to stimulate the appetite for more alcohol, the disease alcoholism would not exist.

But there must be additional factors besides alcohol which enter into the situation. Psychological, emotional, and hormonal influences are doubtless involved and are not by any means ruled out. It seems desirable, however, to stick with the assumption that every disease, including alcoholism, is based upon cell and tissue impairment somewhere in the body. There is no reason why this impairment might not be influenced or even generated by psychological means.

If alcohol produced this same toxic effect (that is, promoting an insatiable appetite for alcohol), equally in all individuals unable to escape this toxicity? The answer must become an alcoholic. This is obviously not so. Why are some individuals unable to escape this toxicity? The answer must lie, it seems, in biochemical individuality. The cells and tissues which govern this appetite mechanism must be peculiarly vulnerable in certain individuals and resistant in others.

Carrying the inquiry still further we may ask, "In what ways can cells be weak and vulnerable, and for what reasons?" Certainly one of the considerations to be thought of in attempting to answer this question is mild malnutrition. Since there are about forty nutrients that cells usually need, and since the short supply of any one can bring weakness, there are in this area numerous potential causes for weakness and vulnerability to the particular type of alcohol poisoning with which we are primarily concerned.

The possibility that nutritional deficiency based upon unusual nutritional needs can be the basic cause of vulnerability in alcoholics is greatly enhanced by the fact that as one consumes more and more alcohol, his or her nutrition becomes progressively worse. Alcohol unquestionably crowds out of the diet wholesome foods which contain minerals, amino acids, and vitamins.

The probability that mild malnutrition is the basic cause of vulnerability in alcoholics is further supported by the fact that, in experimental animals, voluntary consumption of alcohol has been virtually turned off and on, repeatedly, at will, by changing the nutrition of the animals. Good nutrition abolishes their desire to consume alcohol and poor nutrition enhances this desire.

Experimental animals, like humans, have a high degree of biochemical individuality and also have highly distinctive responses to alcohol. When they are placed on a stock diet, they will differ enormously in their voluntary consumption of alcohol; they range from teetotalers to heavy drinkers. This appears to be correlated with the superiority or inferiority of the stock diet for their individual needs. Individual experimental rats are probably more alike than members of the human family, yet they can very readily be demonstrated to have highly distinctive nutritional needs. In recent experiments large numbers of young rats have been fed various diets which are known to be highly deficient. Some rats succumb to malnutrition almost immediately; some resist for a few weeks; others may grow and develop for a much longer time with a surprising approach to good health.

Those whose thinking is oriented along other lines and who are not acquainted with the metabolic unity and diversity that manifests itself in the biological world are prone to ignore the significance of rat experiments because rats under no conditions are real "alcoholics"; their motives and psychological reactions must be vastly different from those of human alcoholics. These objectors may point with some justification to other experiments involving cats, in which frustrations have brought about a desire for alcohol which is perhaps more akin to human alcoholism.

Rat, mouse, guinea pig, hamster, and chick experiments are valuable, since they show clearly that there exists a widespread urge to drink alcohol which has a physiological and biochemical basis. In these animals, as in cats, there seem to be cells and tissues which may become deranged in such a way as to promote an appetite for alcohol. Whether this derangement is likely to be brought about by emotional stress or malnutrition, or both, is something that will differ from species to species and from individual to individual. No one, incidentally, has studied malnutrition in cats as a possible causative factor of alcohol appetite.

Experimental rats have shown variable responses to "psychological" stimuli: some individual animals are induced to drink alcohol when subjected to the stress of noise and flashing lights; others appear to be resistant to this kind of provocation. Poor nutrition, however, always works in the direction of increased alcohol consumption.

It is interesting that, in both humans and experimental animals, appetite derangement in the direction of consuming too much sugar is also induced by poor nutrition and improved by good nutrition. Appetite-controlling cells and tissues, like all other cells, need, if they are to do an all-around good job, adequate amounts of each of about forty nutrients.

The idea that mild cellular malnutrition, based on the unusual nutritional needs of some members of the population, may be the fundamental difficulty in many diseases which have not yet yielded to medical science is one that has not been considered seriously by the medical profession to date. There are many reasons for this. For one thing the nutritional situation is exceedingly complex and is therefore not subject to easy and simple manipulation. Not only does it involve ordinary nutrients, which are needed by the body as a whole, but other nutrients which may not be needed by the body as a whole, but are nonetheless nutritional requirements of certain body cells. Cell nutrients of this type, of which there is an unknown number, must be produced somewhere in the body and thus furnished to the cells that need a supply from outside themselves. Intercellular symbiosis is thus involved, and mild malnutrition in one area may be induced by the failure of cells in another region to export enough of a needed product. The best insurance against failures of this sort is to furnish the body as a whole an abundance of all the needed nutrients, in order that all cells may maintain their maximum health.

Another reason for resistance to the nutritional approach to alcoholism and to many other diseases is the failure to take cognizance of or believe in the facts of biochemical individuality. It is commonly assumed that every so-called normal individual has about the same nutritional requirements. It is also sometimes insisted that the food supply in America is satisfactory and that all that is required for good nutrition is that people eat what is available to them, including all the refined and partially refined foods and drinks which furnish "naked" or nearly naked calories with inadequate supplies of minerals, amino acids, and vitamins. No one who is acquainted with the facts of biochemical individuality, including the wide diversity of needs for individual nutrients, could possibly take such a cavalier attitude toward nutrition. Every study that has been made in the area tends to show that individual people's nutritional needs often differ widely. There is no basis whatever for the assumption that planning for the "average" or "normal" person will take care of the needs of the majority. . . . A most important obstacle in the way of making a reasonable biochemical approach to the subject of alcoholism is the widely and tenaciously held and deeply ingrained assumption that the general concepts of "average person" and "normal person" are quite sound and useful. Actually these expressions are defensible only as long as one is prepared to answer the questions: "Average with respect to what?" and "Normal with respect to what?"

A person may be average or normal with respect to his height, his weight, his cholesterol level, his riboflavin requirement, his calcium needs, or any other single parameter one may chose to measure. The person who is about average with respect to all possible parameters is either nonexistent or else an extraordinarily rare creature. The person who is generally normal in every possible respect would probably be non-existent if one were restrictive in establishing norms, and rare and exceptional even if one were generous in establishing norms. . . .

The question "Why does an 'average' person or a 'normal' person become alcoholic?" makes no sense. In the first place such persons are non-existent or rare; second, if they existed they would not become alcoholics because their reactions to alcohol and everything else would be average or normal. Alcoholism is an individual disease and if we are to search for its roots we must look where the roots are—in certain individuals—not in any hypothetical average creature.

The next question, which is uppermost in many minds, is: "What success has been attained by the nutritional approach to alcoholism?" In answering, the first observation to be made is: *The nutritional approach has seldom been tried.* Seldom, that is, in terms of the millions of individuals who have an alcoholism problem. Scores of individuals have made at least partial trials, with tremendous success. In some cases every testimony is that abolishment of the appetite for alcohol has been complete and lasting, something little short of miraculous. In other cases the help has been less dramatic. I know of no one who has attempted seriously to follow a sensible nutritional regimen who has not appeared to receive substantial benefit.

Of course the ruling out of suggestion and psychological factors in human experiments is no easy task. Several years ago a controlled experiment was attempted to test whether vitamin administration alone—one facet of the nutritional approach—would be effective in controlling alcoholism in an out-patient group.[3] The net result of the study was indicative that the treatment was beneficial, but this was by no means conclusive. Subjects disappeared and diminished in numbers, many failed to take the supplements, some were shifted from one group to another for humanitarian reasons, and various other complications arose which made the experiment fail to reach its objective.

The statistical handling of such an experiment, where numbers are often necessarily distressingly small, is by no means a simple matter. When individuality is so intimately involved as it is in the alcoholism problem, one can hardly hope for an unequivocal statistical answer.

Let us suppose, for example, that our present nutritional knowledge would allow us to correct the trouble in only 10 percent of cases. This would certainly be a partial and worthy success, but it would be exceedingly difficult to get a statistically significant affirmative answer in a situation of this sort.

What proportion of alcoholics would be relieved by a present-day, protracted, thoroughgoing nutritional attack on their disease is unknown. My estimate, based on many observations, is that at least 50 percent would be dramatically benefited and that all the others would receive some benefit. If these estimates are too high *as of now*, there is good reason to believe that within a decade nutritional knowledge will advance so that they will be surpassed.

A matter of very great concern is the oncoming crop of new alcoholics, who year by year more than fill the gaps made by the death of the present victims. Hundreds of thousands of men and women not now alcoholics will become alcoholics—unless something is done about it—in another year or two.

Here there is an excellent chance that the nutritional approach can make a tremendous contribution. Reasonable and particular care about the quality of the food consumed is entirely incompatible with the development of alcoholism. Those who suppose, as a matter of course, that it is all right for a "normal" person to take one drink after another—as many as can be contained without overt and offensive drunkenness—are not thinking in terms of proper nutrition. Nutrition is as far removed from their concern as are the wild flowers of Patagonia.

It is difficult, admittedly, to get those who have alcohol problems to follow reasonable nutritional recommendations. This is to a large extent because of public and professional indifference and unconcern about nutrition. If nutrition were "in the air"—in the thinking of large numbers of intelligent people—the practical trial and application of the nutritional approach would be vastly easier.

As an illustration of how nutrition is neglected, a recent brochure written by a physician on what could be done for alcoholism failed to mention nutrition or to suggest in any way that it could possibly make the slightest difference. We hear a great deal these days about the physical fitness (or unfitness) of our youth. The importance of exercise is stressed and this is good, but one hears no mention of the possibility that what the children eat may make any difference in their fitness. Nutrition is forced to take a back seat in our thinking.

Recent experiments in the laboratory of the Clayton Foundation strongly and compellingly suggest that some individual children are highly vulnerable to deficient diets, while others are relatively resistant. Who wants to take a chance in the hope that his or her child may be resistant?

Most people, through ignorance and neglect, take exactly that chance.

Because of the success I have witnessed in the nutritional combat against alcoholism, I have not the slightest hesitation in recommending to alcoholics, and to those who may have the beginnings of an alcohol problem, that they try the nutritional approach [see Appendix D]. If this recommendation is followed, even with a minimum of understanding, it can do no harm and may salvage the life of the individual.

Nutrition in the Practical Management of Alcoholics

[*Address by Allen A. Parry, M.D., Chief of Alcoholic Service, The Morristown Memorial Hospital, Morristown, New Jersey*]

The subject of nutrition has been so intimately associated with alcoholism that at one time or another all of the manifestations of alcoholism have been attributed to specific deficiencies in nutrition. This includes the most severe complications of liver pathology and central nervous system effects. Specific vitamin deficiencies have long been implicated in many of the varied complications that are seen as a result of alcoholism, and indeed some of these complications have been seen in deficiency states unassociated with the excessive intake of alcohol. The fact that some of these conditions are dramatically improved by the addition of specific vitamins has lent credence to this view. And it is a fact that the administration of suitable nutrients in large amounts still offers the mainstay of treatment in many of the more important complications of alcoholism. All this, of course, does not presume any direct toxic effect of alcohol on these tissues but implies that these manifestations are an indirect effect of malnutrition.

There is recent evidence to indicate that alcohol has direct toxic effects upon the liver, quite apart from the element of malnutrition. The fact that these complications, although in isolated incidences they may occur apart from alcohol, usually are associated with an excessive alcohol intake and sometimes occur even in the presence of what appears to be an adequate diet, indicates that the effect of malnutrition is not the sole damage accomplished by alcohol. It has been shown, for example, that in animals a single severe alcoholic intoxication can result in an abnormal deposition of fat in the liver within hours. Although there is some doubt as to the mechanism of transition from the state of fatty liver to cirrhosis, such a course of events has been observed often enough to suggest that a fatty liver frequently is a precursor of more serious and permanent liver damage. Furthermore, in alcoholics, even after two years of sobriety and an apparently good nutritional state, it has been found that a single moderate dose of alcohol causes effects not found in normal subjects. This demonstrates a direct effect of alcohol on the liver of alcoholics which is not found in nonalcoholic subjects and presumably not based upon a nutritional deficiency. It is quite possible that alcohol also has direct effects upon the central nervous system.

Empirically, it is a fact, however, that even in the more chronic and advanced cases of liver and central nervous system disease, the most important single factor in therapy, aside from the removal of alcohol, lies in attention to adequate nutrition. For example, to the degree that cirrhosis of the liver can be arrested or improved at all, this is accomplished by massive administration of the B vitamins, in addition to a well-rounded intake of the various caloric factors.

Whether these end results of late alcoholism constitute nutritional deficiencies alone or in conjunction with direct toxic effects, the nutritional factor in alcoholics is the end result of a long process of deficiencies in all aspects of nutrition, not of vitamins alone. Most alcoholics take a sufficiently large percentage of their calories in the form of alcohol so that they suffer from inadequate intake of all other useful food substances. . . .

These deficiences start at the point where excessive drinking begins, probably at the point at which the alcoholic responds to hunger by drinking instead of eating. His dietary habits suffer. As he takes more and more of his total calories in terms of alcohol, he gets less and less of the essential protein, fat, vitamins, and minerals, and the more he drinks the more his dietary habits fail. The pattern of drinking in the morning, of skipping breakfast, and of drinking throughout the day with more attention to drinks than to food, is all too familiar. When he stops drinking, frequently the nausea of gastritis interferes with proper nutrition.

Hence the population of any Alcoholic Service in a hospital, with a few outstanding exceptions, consists of people who are either acutely or chronically malnourished. The typical patient has been drinking continuously for more than a week and has not eaten for at least several days. Most of them have a history of alcoholism dating back several years and have not eaten properly during a good deal of that time. Since their caloric intake has probably been adequate, many of them have not, however, lost weight. Alcoholism is one condition, par excellence, where weight is no indication of nutritional adequacy.

The typical entering patient is either intoxicated or very tremulous. . . . The initial treatment is designed to prevent complications of alcohol withdrawal, which include excessive agitation and tremor, convulsions, hallucinosis and, finally, delirium tremens. It consists primarily of adequate sedation, but even in this early period nutrition may play a part. We have found, for example, that the administration of magnesium sulfate completely eliminates alcoholic convulsions. Since this became standard practice on our Alcoholic Service in February 1961, we have not had a single convulsion in the hospital in an alcoholic patient. . . . Some of these patients are sufficiently dehydrated to warrant the administration of intravenous fluids. Rarely more than one such infusion is required, although we have found that in diabetics such infusions, covered with appropriate amounts of regular insulin, frequently effect rapid improvement. Incidentally, we have found the incidence of diabetes in alcoholics to be very low . . . only one diabetic in our hospital population of alcoholics had his disease sufficiently severely to require insulin for daily control. In this connection, it is a well-known fact that very few Jewish people become alcoholics, whereas the incidence of diabetes in Jewish people is relatively high.

The amount of sedation is regulated so as to keep the patient more or less somnolent during the first twenty-four to forty-eight hours, but again it is desirable that he can be aroused for meals and for other vital functions. . . . The usual error made by those not experienced in caring for alcoholics is to give too little sedation.

Multiple vitamin preparations are administered in addition to a regular high protein diet. Hence from the time of admission of the acute alcoholic, some attention is paid to nutrition. One of the notable facts observed during the convalescence of these people is an enormous increase in appetite which is apparently stimulated by the use of extra vitamins. In cases in which a prompt increase in appetite during the first few days has not occurred, it has nearly always been found that the supplementary vitamins have inadvertently been omitted. We therefore routinely administer therapeutic vitamins three times a day. . . .

Our patients' average length of stay in the hospital is between ten and fourteen days. During this period many of the chemical findings return to normal. In those with enlarged livers, the size of that organ has usually decreased nearly to normal unless chemical evidence of cirrhosis is present. The so-called fatty liver is usually reversible if further alcohol is not consumed.

After hospitalization these patients are discharged to our Alcoholic Clinic and managed the same as patients who have presented themselves at the clinic and not been hospitalized. In clinic management of alcoholic patients, a high-protein diet is stressed, with carbohydrates restricted and, in the

form of sugar at least, reserved for those times when the patient feels the impulse to take a drink. The metabolism of
glucose in the body more closely approximates that of alcohol
than any other food stuff, and the administration of sugar
often relieves the craving for alcohol. This can be in the form
of candy, soft drinks, ice cream, honey, or, indeed, lump
sugar.

Attention as to the timing of food intake is also important. These patients are urged to eat at least three times a
day, stress being placed on an adequate breakfast which so
many of them have been in the habit of omitting or slighting.
Female alcoholics frequently tend to omit breakfast, and a
lowering of blood sugar below normal at any time of day
increases the desire for alcohol. Every patient who comes to
our Service is given a special printed form containing dietary
and nutritional recommendations. It includes the recommendation that every meal should include some protein, it outlines the management of carbohydrates, and includes recommendations as to vitamin therapy. . . .

The value of vitamin supplements has been abundantly
demonstrated in our experience. Even in patients in whom
there has been no recent alcoholic intake there is a very evident increase in appetite and a sense of well-being, a finding
not present in non-alcoholics. There is, hence, an increase in
weight, even in those who are not underweight in the beginning of treatment. That there is a specific effect of adequate
vitamin therapy on the desire to drink cannot be denied. In
numerous instances, the patients themselves have attributed
an alcoholic "slip" to temporary cessation of vitamin intake,
and a subsequent ability to abstain to the reinstitution of
vitamins. The nutritional therapy we have learned to employ
was inspired by *Alcoholism: The Nutritional Approach.*[4]

While it is a marked fact, then, that the alcoholic who is
properly nourished finds it much easier to abstain from alcohol, this situation must not be confused with a cure for

alcoholism. Such controlled patients, when they start to drink, develop the same compulsion that they had previously experienced, and attention must be paid to them in areas other than nutrition. The use of tranquilizers is of proven value in helping to manage these people. . . . Whenever the patients have an urge to drink they are instructed to take an extra dose of the tranquilizer together with a readily available source of sugar. This regime has been found to be very effective in reducing daytime tensions, to which alcoholics are so notably subject.

In addition, many alcoholics have become so accustomed to taking a few drinks at bedtime that, when alcohol is withdrawn, they tend to develop insomnia. Sedatives at bedtime counteract this tendency and help to get them through nights without drinking, which are otherwise their most difficult times. However, sleep habits are fairly easily reestablished and night-time medication ordinarily does not have to be continued as long as daytime tranquilization.

One of the most important functions of the physician (and every patient in our out-patient Clinic is seen by a physician at every visit) is, of course, counseling. We feel that in most instances alcoholism is not primarily a psychiatric problem. Such emotional problems as the alcoholic has have usually been created by his drinking rather than being the cause of it. In addition to being kept off alcohol, the patient, as well as other members of his family, usually needs intelligent, sympathetic understanding and counseling with respect to personal, family, sexual, social, employment, and sometimes legal problems. We have found that the effectiveness of out-patient management is directly proportional to the frequency with which patients are seen.

Family and associates must be taught to accept relapses as unfortunate but not as unexpected turns of events. Relapses are self-induced in most chronic diseases as much as they are in alcoholism. The man who has suffered a heart attack and has spent a period of convalescence, after which he feels well and does more and more until he gets a relapse; or the diabetic who gradually eases off his diet until he again requires hospitalization; or the patient with tuberculosis who has been sheltered for months, then increases his activity and cuts corners with his physical care until he gets a relapse—all these are in the same position as the alcoholic who, having been controlled for a period of time, thinks he can drink a little and get away with it and thus initiates a relapse of his disease. Relapses are not a necessary part of the management of this disease; however, they are often a necessary part of the patient's education, in that each one brings home to him again the impossibility of any course other than continuing abstinence as a method of control. Such relapses, then, while they are not pleasant either to the patient or to his associates, are not to be treated as major catastrophes nor the preceding periods of sobriety as time irrevocably lost.

Finally, in the out-patient management of these patients, they are never discharged. They must be followed, although it may be at decreasing intervals, indefinitely. Further, they can be instructed to contact the physician at any time they get into trouble with alcohol, even at the very start of a drinking episode.

With this combined approach of medication, counseling, and nutrition, good results are obtained in 50 to 70 percent of the total number of patients seen. The element of this approach that is most frequently slighted by other treating agencies is the nutritional factor. Patients may voluntarily stop their medications, and they may fail to return for counseling, but once they have become accustomed to taking vitamins, they practically never stop if they are really serious about controlling their drinking.

The fact that adequate diet and vitamins make it easier for the alcoholic to stay off alcohol is certainly of some importance. However, it must never be forgotten that these people, though their disease may be controlled, are still alcoholics. Control must never be confused with cure, nor factors producing complications with causation. The cause of alcoholism is not yet known. Biochemists believe that it will be found to be due to alterations in biochemistry, probably on a genetic basis. The psychiatrists are equally certain that the basic defect lies in their field. Certainly most of the complications are due to specific nutritional defects, most of them in terms of vitamins and amino acids. As a treating agency whose main purpose is to get these patients well and to keep them well, we must empirically use the methods that have been found to correct most of their symptoms. But we must recognize that the nutrition in alcoholics is very like the use of insulin and other agents in diabetes, in that these control the patient without any reference to the real cause of his disease.

The alcoholic must be as basically different from the normal as is the diabetic. Furthermore, we must guard against comparing the findings in experimental animals, however treated, with those in alcoholic humans. No one has ever created an alcoholic animal. The management of animals on deficient diets is analogous to the management of patients, not with primary alcoholism but with some of the dietary complications of this disease. It is becoming increasingly apparent that while we can manage deficiency states in alcoholism, they may bear little relation to the cause of this disease. If alcoholics as a group paid as much attention to nutrition as do diabetics, probably as many would be as well controlled. We must not forget that we are dealing with patients as whole people, from all walks of life. Until such time as we can deal with the cause of this disease, we must not only take care of its complications in terms of nutrition, but must also instill into each patient a philosophy of living with his disease and must give him constant support in terms of the frustrations he encounters in his family, social, and business life.

Experiments in Treating Alcoholics with
Glutamic Acid and Glutamine

[*Address by Louis P. Fincle, M.D., Veterans Administration Hospital, New Bedford, Massachusetts*]

The treatment of alcoholism has been a world-wide controversial and unresolved problem since the effects of alcohol were first discovered by man. This has mainly been complicated by the numerous theories concerning the causes of alcoholism, whereby no single factor could be isolated as the basis for the disorder referred to as alcohol addiction. In our present state of knowledge, alcoholism is a disorder of unknown cause, and its treatment is non-specific and varies with the presenting symptoms. . . .

When one stops to realize the size of the problem of alcoholism, does one begin to wonder why further progress has not been made in stemming this disorder which appears to be increasing with each new generation?

The current treatments, including sedatives, tranquilizers, electro-shock, psychoanalysis, hypnosis, LSD, and medical treatment with vitamins and nutritious fluids, have failed to be effective or definitive. The best that has been accomplished by these methods of treatment was to allay the symptoms without effecting the craving or the inability to stop drinking. The same results have been accomplished by legal, moral, and punitive pressures.

Recent biochemical studies have revealed that the alcoholic invariably showed evidence of a nutritional defect or impaired bodily function due to a nutritional disorder. It was hypothesized that the nutritional defect may be the basis for the craving for alcohol. Whether this was an inherent nutritional defect, or whether certain cells in the brain, liver, or other organs were affected by a nutritional disorder that created the physiological urge to drink, still remains uncertain.

In view of the nutritional theory concerning the basis for

alcoholism I undertook a series of experimental studies utilizing nutritional substances (glutamic acid derivatives) to
determine the effect on the craving for alcoholic beverages in
hospitalized alcoholic addicts. The nutritional substances
were known to exist in the brain, liver, and intestines in
liberal quantities under normal conditions. Another important
aspect in the use of these nutritional substances was that they
were non-toxic and were without serious side effects as compared with drugs.

The first study consisted of 10 hospitalized psychiatric
male patients with severe alcohol problems, whose hospitalization was due to their acutely disturbed behavior or sui-
cidal tendencies while under the influence of alcoholic beverages. These patients ranged in age from 27 to 48 years, were
of average intelligence, had an extensive history of alcoholism, and were classified as alcohol addicts in addition to their
psychiatric illness. They were a difficult problem in management due to their disturbed "acting out," hostile and
manipulative behavior requiring maximum security measures.

This group of patients was given for three to four
months a course of treatment with a substance called L-glutamine. This substance is known to exist in the human brain
in high concentration. The specific nature of its action still
remains unclear, but it is known to participate in the complex
chemical processes in the brain which have to do with the
nutrition required in brain functioning.

Throughout the study the patients were closely observed
for any evidence of untoward reactions. To evaluate mean-
ingfully the effects of the treatment on the patient's alcoholic
habits and behavior, they were permitted after a test period
of two weeks to leave the maximum security ward for visits
outside the hospital as well as weekend visits.

Seven of the 10 patients manifested some form of improvement in their alcoholic habits, from total abstinence to
varying degrees of control in their alcoholic indulgence and
behavior. However, following discontinuance of the sub-

stance, the 7 improved patients gradually resumed their former alcoholic habits after a two- to twelve-month period.

Further study is indicated to determine whether continued usage of this substance would have had a more sustained effect on their alcoholic habits. It is encouraging to note that several of the patients stated that the "craving for drink" was absent while they were taking the substance during the period of the study. No ill effects from the substance were noted throughout the study.

The second study evolved from the theory held by some investigators that nutritional deficiencies in alcoholics are the basis for, or participate in, the development of alcoholism. Certain physical and mental disorders associated with alcoholism are said to be attributed to a nutritional deficiency, especially to a deficiency of the vitamin B complex.

This second study consisted of 26 hospitalized psychiatric patients with alcohol problems, referred to as spree drinkers, or chronic alcoholics, as differentiated from the more serious addicted alcoholic. The patients were divided into two matched groups of 13, labeled A and B. The matching was done on the basis of age, length of hospital stay, and drinking behavior pattern. The ages ranged from 28 to 66 years, with the median age of 45.

Group A received a mixture of a substance called sodium glutamate combined with B-complex vitamins. Sodium glutamate enters the circulation as glutamic acid, which also participates in the brain chemistry in a similar manner to L-glutamine. Group B received only the B-complex vitamins.

Patients in both groups were evaluated as to their alcoholic habits after receiving the nutritional substances for three months.

Of the 13 patients in Group A, 8 manifested improvement in their drinking habits, while only 2 of the 13 patients in Group B showed improvement. The improvement ranged from total abstinence to mild, moderate drinking without the ill effects manifested from drinking prior to the study. As in the previous study, the drinking habits were again resumed following termination of the study period.

The third study was to test the prevailing psychological and "punitive" method of treatment for the alcoholic, utilizing psychological methods in a controlled and restricted environment. An intensive treatment program was set up with a goal toward rehabilitation and discharge within a three-month period.

The treatment program in which each patient was expected to participate consisted of the following:

Daily six-hour manual work detail

Group psychotherapy for one hour twice a week

Conferences with social worker toward establishing suitable living arrangements in the community

Conferences with the vocational psychologist toward evaluating patient's qualifications and capacities for employment and assisting patient in obtaining suitable employment.

Each patient was accorded privileges and passes if he cooperated with the program and maintained sobriety. If he became intoxicated, these privileges were revoked for two weeks. Medication was prescribed as needed.

This group consisted of 20 male patients similar to the patients in the previous study—spree drinkers or chronic alcoholics.

The poorest results were obtained with this study. Only 3 out of the group of 20 manifested improvement in their drinking habits during the three-month period. These results parallel the treatment of the alcoholic by the courts, whereby an alcoholic who is arrested repeatedly for drunkenness is hailed before the judge and, if found to be a chronic offender, is either sentenced to jail for a variable period of time or remanded to an alcoholic clinic for psychological treatment.

It must be emphasized that these three studies collectively do not constitute sufficient evidence for the rational treatment of alcohol addiction or the more widespread chronic alcoholism. However, the results do bring out the need for more concentrated research and study of this grave disorder, whether it be a symptom of an underlying psychological defect, biochemical defect, or both.

The following table summarizes the results of the three studies described:

	GLUTAMINE		GLUTAMATE		PSYCHOTHERAPY	
	No.	Percent	No.	Percent	No.	Percent
Controlled	4	40	4	33	3	15
Improved	3	30	4	33	0	0
Unchanged	3	30	2	17	11	55
Worse	0		2	17	6	30
Total	10		12		20	
Dropouts	0		1		0	

Due to the limited scope of these studies, opinion as to the specific value of the methods in the treatment of alcoholism must be reserved until many more specific studies are done. However, these studies do indicate that the least effective treatment appears to be the psychological method. This is corroborated in clinical practice by the poor results, as evidenced by frequent relapses, obtained with the alcoholics treated in psychologically oriented alcohol clinics and private practice. This observation is not intended to be critical of this form of treatment; it is rather an indication of the alcoholic's unresponsiveness to this treatment in general as well as his resentment to the punitive measures imposed upon him by the courts.

The treatment of the alcoholic is most difficult and frustrating, as he tends to be unreliable, uncooperative, and demanding, has a low tolerance for stress, and will frequently sabotage the treatment regime. This behavior or personality disorder is probably due to the alcoholic's marked dependency needs which only alcohol seems to relieve. It may be hypothesized that the substances used in the first two studies may aid in alleviating these dependency feelings and thus relieve the craving for alcohol. However, these are only adjunctive measures. It is the opinion of many researchers in the field of medicine today that alcoholism is more likely due to multiple causes and requires the intensive treatment of many disciplines, with the medical, psychological, social, religious, and legal professions working together.

It is hoped that these studies will stimulate further investigations in the field of alcoholism so that proper preventive measures may be formulated to stem this progressive disorder—whether it be a symptom or disease entity—which threatens the health and welfare of future generations. This threat is clearly illustrated by the increase in the chronic incapacitated alcoholics being admitted to our mental hospitals today—patients who are permanently and totally incapacitated and will require institutional care for the remainder of their lives due to permanent brain damage.

The current status of the treatment of alcoholism can be described as at best meeting with minimal or insignificant success. Yet, despite the numerous alcohol clinics throughout the country, lay organizations and intensive educational drives, including a period of prohibition in the past, as well as the use of every known means of communication, alcoholism continues uncontrolled and threatening to the health and welfare of our society. . . . It is hoped that additional governmental aid and further research may develop newer and more effective drugs, a better understanding of the role of nutritional substances, and better psychological techniques. We have the means to treat the symptoms of alcoholism, but the cure will come in the discovery and specific treatment of its causes or basis.

* 5

A FAMILY ILLNESS

One of the most insidious things about alcoholism is that it leaves its imprint on everything and everyone it touches. Its immediate victims are the nation's five or six million citizens now suffering from the disease; in addition, it indirectly injures many times that number—the wives, husbands, children, employers, and friends of the alcoholic.

No one can question the fact that alcoholism is a family illness in every sense of the term. Dr. Marvin A. Block has stated: "The cost of alcoholism may be a drastically curtailed career, the destruction of plans for a child's education, the breakdown of family and social life, and the survival of the family itself." [1]

Contrary to popular belief, the majority of men and women suffering from alcoholism in this country today are married. They are in the early or middle stages of their illness, have homes, and, until the progression of the illness has reached the chronic stages, they have jobs. Since accurate surveys have shown that alcoholism occurs most often between ages thirty and fifty-five and develops in all social and economic backgrounds, irrespective of education, occupation, or financial resources, the illness has a particularly sharp impact on the family.

Even when drinking has been a problem for a man before marriage, his wife may not have recognized this fact during courtship or even for some years after the wedding. The development of this illness is often slow, and its telltale symptoms are not known by many people and not apparent even to close associates for varying lengths of time.

118

Impact on Family Life

Professor Harrison M. Trice of Cornell University has described the impact of alcoholism upon the other members of the family: [2]

> Developing alcoholics are often charming people, and many people who are not alcoholics drink to excess on social occasions. Soon, however, the spouse begins to notice embarassing incidents, usually in a social situation. . . . At first the spouse may overlook these deviant actions, but, as they recur, he or she begins to worry about the opinion of other people. . . . If it is the husband who has the drinking problem, the wife may recruit the family doctor to provide legitimate "sick" diagnoses for her husband's "unbearable employer" who "causes him to drink too much now and then." Children's queries receive vague and indefinite answers.
>
> As her attempts to contain the problem repeatedly fail, so does her rapport with her husband deteriorate. Less and less does he fill the role of father and husband, and more and more she must take over both male and female family roles. Throughout this early period the family remains intact. In devising ways of getting on with family living, the wife begins to derive her emotional support and satisfaction from her children, not her alcoholic spouse.
>
> As the wife is struggling to maintain the former family pattern, outside forces move the family into a middle period of adjustment. Friends include them less and less in drinking-group situations, and both the wife and her drinking husband withdraw more and more and participate less in outside activities in an effort to cover up and avoid further humiliation. The exclusion from friendship groups serves to verify the wife's fear about her husband's drinking. . . . Conflicts over the children pervade this period. The wife's concern for them and the deep split with her husband often lead to a search for outside help. . . .

When the wife partly stabilizes the family without her husband, she re-establishes some faith in herself and provides a basis for rethinking the situation. Perhaps reading about alcoholism or talking with doctors, ministers, local agencies, or members of Alcoholics Anonymous will lead her to discover that treatment facilities do exist for her alcoholic husband. She may learn that she need not cover up or be ashamed, at which point she may decide to remain married. If so, she must continue to manage the family during her husband's therapy. . . .

From marital statistics it is clear that often the wife decides to terminate the marriage. She has discovered that while she is managing on her own, her family runs more smoothly and she has more security. She believes that her children have a more consistent and less confusing environment.

In sum, it seems doubtful that wives are deeply upset at the beginning of their husband's drinking problem. On the other hand, the demands to adjust to new family roles created by living with an alcoholic spouse could result in personality disturbance. Although far less is known about husbands of alcoholic women, it seems probable that living through the experience leaves the husband just as disorganized.

Much the same can be said about children of alcoholics —especially if the alcoholic is their mother. If they are infants or quite young, or if they are well into adolescence, the damage to them may be less; but in pre-adolescent years they suffer a variety of emotional handicaps. An alcoholic parent deprives children of adult role models. They also experience the social ostracism of the family, the intensity of which varies; it can be damaging to a child's self-image and can sharply limit normal interpersonal experiences.

What Can Be Done Constructively?

The most constructive step which members of the family can take is to motivate the person suffering from alcoholism toward proper treatment. After treatment has begun, their next job is to work cooperatively with the sick member in providing sympathy, understanding, and approval during the crucial period of convalescence toward ultimate recovery.

While these steps may seem simple, they are usually difficult to execute because of the complex nature of alcoholism as a disease and the general lack of knowledge about alcohol and its insidious effects. Certainly the wife and children of the alcoholic cannot be criticized for their lack of knowledge concerning this vital family problem.

Serious difficulties are involved when a spouse and other family members are faced with the necessity of explaining to the sick person that not only is he or she seriously ill, but, for the sake of all concerned, must seek treatment before it is too late. Says Dr. Marvin A. Block:

Admittedly, it is difficult to label as alcoholic someone you have known for a long time and with whom you have shared a great deal of pleasure—indeed, someone with whom you have drunk. It is even more difficult to label oneself an alcoholic when one can see no difference between one's own drinking and that of so many of one's companions. The slight shadings and differences between the early alcoholic and the heavy social drinker are so vague and so small that differentiation between the two is difficult.[3]

Nevertheless the refusal to take the responsibility of labeling has contributed to the progress of the disorder in many individuals. Failure to suggest to someone you know the possibility that his excessive drinking is alcoholism risks his health and happiness; members of his family risk their own as well. The person suffering from alcoholism takes the same risk when he or she refuses to acknowledge that drinking has become uncontrolled. To tell an individual that his drinking has become excessive may incur his resentment, but to avoid this responsibility is to do him a disservice for which one is forever answerable.

Sometimes curiosity can motivate the problem drinker to do something constructive about the situation. For the man or woman still in the denial stage of the illness, a check of the symptoms of alcoholism may provide the impetus to contact Alcoholics Anonymous, visit an Alcoholism Information Center, or consult a physician knowledgeable about the disease. The questionnaire in Appendix B provides such a check.

Two Great Resources for the Family

In many areas of the United States where Alcoholics Anonymous groups exist, there are also Al-Anon family groups, an invaluable aid to spouses of alcoholics, whether the person has stopped drinking or not, and Alateen groups for young people seeking help with the problems created by an alcoholic parent or close relative. (See Appendix D.) Al-Anon is a fellowship for relatives and friends of alcoholics, corresponding in philosophy, structure, and program to the related and better-known fellowship of Alcoholics Anonymous. Most Al-Anon members are wives of alcoholics, although the groups include husbands of women alcoholics and other relatives.

There is no background requirement for seeking Al-Anon's help. The alcoholic spouse may or may not be a member of AA. According to the organization's own statement of purpose, Al-Anon members "are banded together to solve their common problems of fear, insecurity, lack of understanding of the alcoholic and of the warped relationships associated with alcoholism."

The first contact with Al-Anon usually engenders hope in the despairing spouse of an alcoholic. He or she learns that the causes of the alcoholism lie far deeper than the marriage partner's own behavior and attitudes in his or her efforts to control the drinking. If the problem is that of a wife with an alcoholic husband, she also discovers that any effective decision must come from him, but that meanwhile there are many things she can do to change her own attitudes and create a better life for herself and her children, even if her husband continues to drink. The same principle applies if the situation is reversed, and the alcoholic spouse is the wife.

Al-Anon may thus be characterized as a self-help fellowship in which, with understanding people, new activities, and new friends, the spouse of an alcoholic may gain strength to look at the problem objectively, realizing that others have faced and adjusted to it. The spouse is no longer trapped inside the family dilemma, but is outside and not alone. If the alcoholic partner has not already sought treatment through AA or some other community facility, the understanding gained by the spouse from the experience of fellow members of Al-Anon often motivates such a course. For some members Al-Anon becomes a way of life with deep spiritual implications, very much as AA does for some alcoholics.

Alateen groups consist of young people between the ages of twelve and twenty. Anyone in this age group is eligible for membership. There are no dues or fees. Alateen members meet to exchange experiences and to gain an understanding of alcoholism. This helps them keep their own lives and personal development from being too deeply affected by close association with an alcoholic. They learn to detach themselves emotionally from the difficulties of their parents, while continuing to love them. As older people do in Al-Anon, young people benefit beyond an understanding of the disease and how to adjust to it, acquiring an objective viewpoint toward the problem. Alateen helps teen-agers to analyze their own faults and failures and to determine to what extent these are caused by living where alcoholism exists. It inspires a desire for personal improvement through more sympathetic understanding of others. The teen-agers also are not alone, caught in a dilemma without help. Alateen helps them get outside themselves and realize they can build their own lives purposefully. In the meantime family affairs may right themselves; but their own lives will benefit from overcoming what seemed inescapable adversity.

Both the spouse, through Al-Anon, and the children, through Alateen, benefit in ways far beyond the practical help in dealing with the problem of alcoholism at home. They can find inspiration to become better people themselves and thus enrich their own lives. Helpful pamphlets on various aspects of alcoholism within the family circle have been published by Al-Anon (see Selected Reading List).

How the Family Can Work Together

Taking constructive action against a common problem brings a feeling of relief and a sense of purpose to any group of people. These benefits are especially evident in a family unit which has been able to work together to overcome the problem of alcoholism. When the ill member is embarked on a course of treatment which may bring about total recovery, and the other members of the family are aware of their proper roles in stabilizing family relationships, the rest becomes simply a matter of time and effort. The family is on the right track again.

Impossible as it might have seemed a few weeks or months earlier, the impact of alcoholism on family life can sometimes prove a benefit rather than a disaster. Through successfully resisting alcoholism as a threat to the survival of family life, each member may find new ways to improve his or her own daily life.

With new attitudes toward other people, the discovery and correction of individual weaknesses and faults, the removal of self-pity and the gaining of a constructive attitude toward life and its problems, every member of the family can actually profit from this experience.

As for the family member recovering from the disease of alcoholism, the simple fact that he or she is trying to do something about the condition, on a day-to-day basis, is its own reward. No one can fail to benefit in character, in inner worth, or in outward contacts with other people, from such a sustained effort. The program outlined in Chapter 2 presents constructive suggestions for individual action and for rebuilding family relationships.

The Wife's Course of Action

[The following discussion was written by the wife of a recovered alcoholic.]

The wife of an alcoholic has indeed a difficult role. However, there are certain courses of constructive action which can be taken and certain other courses which should be avoided.

Usually, when confronted with the husband's alcoholism, the wife tries to dominate her husband, or protect him. Experience has shown that neither of these courses of action will work.

First of all, the wife has to find out all the facts about what it is that confronts her. In other words, she needs much information about alcohol and alcoholism. [Sources of information have already been mentioned in this chapter; see also Appendix D.]

Through the information she receives, she will be confirmed in her judgment that this is a family disease and that she has a part to play. She will find out the interaction of the illness within the family and her part in accepting the alcoholic as a sick person and in making the recovery easier.

Armed with these facts, the wife will also learn the important steps to recovery. First, the alcoholic must be left to solve his own problems; they are his problems, not his wife's, and he must deal with them himself. The alcoholic must be made to feel responsible for his own life and therefore his own recovery. He must make the decision to drink or not to drink. During this period, the wife cannot scold, plead, reason, or threaten her husband into sobriety but should maintain a positive attitude, knowing that alcoholism is an illness that can be arrested. For her own strength and peace of mind, a detachment from the present difficulties is beneficial, and the development of a sense of her own worth, with her own emotional outlets, aids her tranquillity. Such an attitude will often give strength and freedom to the alcoholic husband and hasten his decision to give up alcohol.

The next step is for the wife to steel herself against possible crises. The drinking situation usually gets worse before it gets better. This is known as "reaching a bottom." Usually outside circumstances create the bottom—physical illness, loss of job, loss of self-respect. Sometimes, if all else fails, the wife has to create the bottom by demanding either sobriety or separation—perhaps divorce.

Then the husband usually finds there is no way to go but up—to a life of usefulness and sobriety. During this last step—the recovery—patience and support on the wife's part are necessary. There should be demonstration of affection and a sense of working together. Now there can be a happy use of leisure time—the time that was formerly spent in drinking can now be used for new pursuits and interests.

In summary, after the wife finds out all she can about alcoholism, she should then decide upon four important steps in her role as wife:

1. Make the alcoholic husband take the responsibility for his own actions.

2. Develop in herself a feeling of independence from the conflict, a detachment from her husband's problem, together with a sense of her own worth and interests.

3. Be willing to "create a bottom," if all else fails.

4. Lend support during recovery, so that husband and wife may work together toward an even happier married life.

Case Histories

I. A YOUNG WOMAN WITH A PROBLEM

[*This case was reported by an authority in the field of alcoholism.*]

Some years ago the daughter of a great friend of mine called me to say that she had a problem she would like to discuss with me. We made an appointment for the following afternoon. When Jane arrived around five o'clock, she looked perfectly lovely. She was twenty-eight, married, with two handsome children, a fine house, and supposedly at the beginning of her prime of life, both physically and mentally. I asked what her problem was. Although I have been working in the field of alcoholism many years, her answer came as a great surprise. She said, "I think I may be coming down with alcoholism, and I would like to tell you about my symptoms."

Since I had never seen this girl the slightest bit under the influence of alcohol, I could hardly believe my ears. She went on to explain: "I find that after I have a drink, I can't stop until I go to bed. The result is that, as I don't want to get tight in public, I don't take my first drink until just before dinner in the evening. If there are cocktails served for some time before a dinner party, I will wait until dinner is announced before having my drink. Then I will drink wine with dinner, a liqueur after dinner, and a couple of highballs after that. It is then time to go home and I can handle this much without showing it. However, on arriving home, I need a drink and will usually drink until I am intoxicated. This, of course, makes my husband terribly upset.

"It is a little easier to cover up when I have guests in. I follow the same system, but I can usually sneak my drinks after the guests go home while I am tidying up the house for the next day. My husband now has caught on to this also, and, although I believe he really loves me, I am so repulsive to him when I get drunk that he won't even sleep in the same room with me. He told me to come and see you today, and has told me that unless I seek help with my drinking problem, he will have to leave me. Do you think I am getting alcoholism?"

I told Jane that in my opinion she did have a real problem and I was happy that she had come to me before it had become more serious. I knew that two members of her family had died of alcoholism, and although we are not sure that tendency to the illness is inherited, we do know it runs very strongly in certain families. I asked Jane if she wanted the full treatment in learning to live happily without alcohol, or whether she would just like to read some literature and perhaps see an internist and psychiatrist for a physical and mental inventory. Jane said she knew that alcoholism was a respectable, treatable illness and she wanted to do everything necessary to get over it just as soon as possible. I proceeded to explain the Alcoholics Anonymous program to her, and she found it interesting, so we made plans for her treatment.

I set up an appointment for her with a doctor who would give her a physical examination, also an appointment with a psychiatrist for one session. I made arrangements for her to attend meetings of an AA group in which she would find a number of people of about her own age.

The physical examination disclosed no damage. She was given an A-1 bill of health. The psychiatric evaluation revealed that she was rather shy, and it was suggested that during her first few months of sobriety she cut down on social events. Jane and her husband had been going with rather a fast set, and a further suggestion was that they try to make friends with a more conservative group.

The AA meetings were a great success, and Jane took to them "like a duck to water." Four years after our original talk, I am glad to be able to report that Jane and her husband are extremely happy. She had a third baby two years ago and a fourth will be born in a couple of months. Jane and her husband mingle socially with friends, but these are more conservative than the previous group. It is true that the couple skips some cocktail parties, and if they think there is going to be a rather long cocktail hour before dinner, they may arrive for only the last few minutes of the drinking. During the day, when many of Jane's friends are playing bridge and drinking, she uses the time to work constructively for various charities. She is one of the most popular members of the community.

It is a pleasure to be able to tell this story. It shows that the younger generation really believes that alcoholism is a respectable illness and not something to be put up with in shame and fear of discovery. Because Jane has told her friends that she is an alcoholic, she has also had the added satisfaction of being in a position to help others.

II. CHILDREN PRESENT A UNITED FRONT

When George Grant was young, he was painfully shy, particularly in the presence of girls. He envied very much the friendly and easy way that some of his friends could get along with the opposite sex. Although he wanted to, he was too shy to put his arm around a girl or tell her that he liked her.

During the Christmas vacation when he was eighteen, he went to a series of parties in New York, staying at a hotel with his roommate from boarding school. He noticed one evening that his friend was being much bolder than usual and, when they went home, he discussed this with him. He found that his roommate had gone to a speakeasy with a girl around midnight and had a martini, and that this one drink had made it possible for him to talk and dance much better and have an extra-good time. The next night George and his friend visited the bar, and George had his first drink. The result was even more gratifying than his friend had predicted. For the first time in his life he really had a good time with the girls at the dance. He even took one home and kissed her goodnight.

The different reactions of George and his roommate to the effects of alcohol are significant. The latter, who remained a social drinker all his life, found the unaccustomed martini made for more fun at a party, enabled him to improve his dancing, and thus heightened his enjoyment. For him drinking simply provided a social lubricant. But for George alcohol's effect really provided a miracle. It transformed him from an awkward adolescent, very conscious of his pimples, into a self-confident "passable" dancer, more at ease with his feminine partners. What alcohol did for George, even at this early age, was to provide him with an approximation of the sort of personality and self-confidence he had always envied in others. Many recovered alcoholics have reported that from the very beginning alcohol seemed to "do more" for them than for other people. Hence its fatal lure which eventually leads to dependence.

For the first few years alcohol stood George in good stead. He was able to speak fairly well at business meetings if he had had a few drinks, and he could be more at ease at social gatherings. However, by the time he was about thirty, drink was no longer all pleasure. Bad hangovers were setting in. Occasionally he would do silly things in the evenings and not remember them the next day. A year or so later, while working as head of one of the branches of his father's company, he was arrested for drunken driving. Fearing that his father would fire him, he sent a lawyer to visit the arresting officer. The attorney persuaded the policeman and his family to accept a suitable Christmas present. When the case came to court, the policeman apologized for losing his temper, and the case was dismissed.

During World War II the progression of George's drinking was temporarily controlled by fear of being court-martialed. However, since he had a desk job, he consumed a great deal of beer and ale. When he came out of the service he was thirty pounds overweight and unable to wear any of his civilian clothes. To lose weight, he went to a health resort but did not tell the doctor that he was a heavy drinker. As a result he was given too limited a diet, with no liquor and reduced calories of food. When a doctor knows that his overweight patient has a drinking problem, he first forbids liquor; usually the desired weight loss will follow. Food intake should never be cut down at the same time that alcohol is given up. In George's case the results of the too severe regimen were dehydration and gumboils. The latter were so painful that, on leaving the health resort, George went back to drinking and for the first time had to be hospitalized for his nerves.

By this time George's father had died and George had become head of his company, a large national organization. He found that he could not drink and work, so he became a periodic drinker. When he was on the wagon he did a fine job. When he was drinking, he was protected by his loyal employees and his family. His drinking had now definitely become a problem.

George Grant was in an unusually dangerous position when he became an alcoholic. He was outside the pressures which can usually be used to motivate action toward recovery. He could not lose his job: he was the head of the company, which was the most successful in that particular industry. His wife, whom he had loved dearly, had recently died after a lingering illness, a circumstance which had made his drinking worse. A widower with three devoted grown children, he was in no danger of losing his home. He was a member of a socially prominent family, was very wealthy, had considerable innate ability, and was such a wonderful man when sober that most of his relatives, friends, and associates were unable to believe that he was a full-fledged alcoholic. Nor did he realize this himself.

He was one of several brothers who had suffered from alcoholism in various stages over a period of years. He himself had for many years blamed his excessive drinking on everything imaginable except the fact that he was actually suffering from alcoholism. Between his drinking bouts, he was genuinely liked by everyone with whom he came in contact. Not even his closest business associates, friends, or worried relatives had the heart to tell him what a problem he was when he drank.

Several years after his wife's death he became interested in a fine woman, but because of his drinking, she was unwilling to marry him. Even this did not convince him that alcohol was affecting his social life and his health, and as head of his company he could not be pressured into treatment under the alcoholism program for employees.

But George Grant was very fortunate in having three intelligent, devoted children, who had made the necessary effort to learn from responsible sources the true nature of their father's illness. These young people had grown up in an age when information on the use of alcohol and the proper approach to the problems of alcoholism had become widespread through newspapers, magazines, television, and radio. While George was visiting friends in Europe, his children consulted professionals skilled in the modern approaches to alcoholism and its treatment—physicians, the medical director of their father's company, and the director of the local Alcoholism Information Center. They also talked with long-time members of Alcoholics Anonymous and attended meetings of Al-Anon groups.

Having gained a true perspective on their father's troubles and what could be done about them, the three went abroad to visit him. One morning while he was sober and composed they spoke to him quietly and unemotionally about his problem. They told him that drinking was ruining his life, upsetting their lives, bewildering his many wonderful friends, and causing a real problem in the company that bore his name. George listened attentively and for the first time in his life recognized that what he actually had was alcoholism. As he thought about the situation, he recalled that several of his friends had recovered from alcoholism without losing top-notch jobs, money, family, or friends.

As soon as the delegation of his children had left the room, he went to the friends whom he was visiting and said, "I have been outvoted. I am finally convinced that I am an alcoholic, and I am going to do everything in my power to recover."

His first step was to return to the United States and go to a hospital to be "dried out." After leaving the hospital, he went to a facility which was recommended for rehabilitation and education about alcoholism.

He has now been sober for several years and is happily married to the fine and intelligent woman who quite rightly refused to marry him while he was still drinking. (Many men and women have made the mistake of thinking that, through mutual love and marriage, the problem of alcoholism will go away. This does not happen.) George's children are very proud that they were able to help their father, whom they have always loved deeply. George, in turn, will be everlastingly grateful to them for telling him candidly what his problem was.

George Grant's story has several important aspects:

1. It illustrates how helpful younger people can be to their parents and friends with alcohol problems, as a result of growing

up unhampered by the old prejudices and regarding alcoholism as a legitimate, treatable disease.

2. By admitting freely to many people that his trouble was alcoholism, from which he was able to recover through a sound and practical program, George has contributed a great deal toward removing the stigma surrounding alcoholism among his colleagues and business associates, many of whom are people who influence opinion in America.

3. His experience greatly strengthens the position held by all prominent workers in the field of alcoholism that, since the disease is respectable and treatable, to "cover up" for friends and relatives suffering from it is unnecessary and endangers their lives. Instead, the problem should be brought into the open in a climate of understanding.

III. THE DOWNWARD SPIRAL

Robert Cutler walked out of his boss's office one afternoon, looking bewildered and apprehensive. He had been promoted and given a raise in salary. For most people such news would have been cause for elation and a celebration. Cutler's reaction might have been the same, since he immediately left the office and sought out a neighborhood bar—a place he knew was not frequented by his business associates. But the difference in Cutler's case was that he needed a drink, and not to celebrate anything. In fact, he was downright fearful. His promotion was from an editorial staff job as a business and financial writer to manager of client relations. It was his third promotion in the six years he had worked for a nationally known magazine. The trouble was that this new job would involve extensive business entertaining, which often included drinking, and Bob Cutler had known for at least two years that somehow he was not able to handle alcohol any more.

His employer did not know this, nor did his associates on the editorial staff. In their company he had always been most careful to confine his drinking to one or two social cocktails. Actually he believed that only his wife, Diane, knew of his bitter problem.

"Why didn't I have the courage to tell Mr. Cox the truth?" thought Cutler, as he ordered a martini. "But I might have been fired, instead of promoted!"

By the time he had ordered his second martini, he felt better. "Think of what this means," he reasoned. "More money, a step nearer executive rank, and now perhaps Diane will be less critical of my behavior, and our bills will be paid more promptly." All traces of apprehension and fear had gone. He had regained his self-confidence, which often deserted him these days but which alcohol seemed to restore. "What is there to be worried about? I'm on the way up, not down!" He finished his third martini and made his way to the railroad terminal. On the train home he did not go near the bar car.

Since Robert Cutler realized that he was having trouble with his drinking, why had he not stopped, or at least tried to control the amount he drank? The answer is that he had tried both these approaches and failed with both. Several times he had gone on the wagon for varying lengths of time and had felt miserable. As for controlled drinking, he had been able to keep to a limit of one or two drinks for a while, then, at a most inopportune time—on an occasion that demanded sobriety—he would become obviously intoxicated. Luckily this had never happened at the office. "Something has happened to my drinking capacity," he often thought, but he had not faced the fact that he was in a serious and dangerous position and had better seek help to stop drinking entirely.

When Cutler reached home that night he told his wife about his new job, with all its implications and dangers. Diane was happy about the promotion but she realized that unless her husband stopped drinking entirely, in the new job the firm would soon become aware of his problem.

Recently, feeling that she must talk to someone outside the family, she had discussed her husband's inability to handle alcohol with her best friend, Ann Ross. Diane had been startled to learn that Ann had been in the same predicament with her own husband and that her problem had been resolved. Alex Ross had joined Alcoholics Anonymous five years earlier and had not had a drink since. Now, Ann had said, the Ross family couldn't be happier.

Diane told Bob what Ann Ross had told her. "Wouldn't it be wonderful if this could happen to us?"

"You mean I should join AA?" Cutler exclaimed. "Why, I never realized that Alex Ross was a member."

"Ann takes a cocktail once in a while but Alex always corrals a soft drink," replied Diane, "and naturally they never discuss the situation publicly."

Bob Cutler was silent for a time. "You really are convinced that I have to give up drinking, aren't you, Diane?" he finally asked. "You know I have tried going on the wagon before and how miserable and ineffectual I have felt. But for you and the children, I'll try again. How do I go about joining AA?"

Ann Ross had told Diane that her husband would be happy to introduce Bob to AA whenever he felt ready. Diane promptly called her friend, and within the hour Alex Ross and Bob Cutler were deep in conversation. Bob started going to AA meetings with Alex as his sponsor. And he did not drink, although the desire was at times almost more than he could bear. One night, as he and Ross were on their way to an AA meeting, Cutler remarked, "It's tough, Alex, but I have to do this for Diane and the children."

"You had better realize right now, Bob, that you are doing this for yourself and no one else. This is a selfish program. We make sobriety the number one project in our lives because we are powerless over alcohol. We in AA sincerely *want* to stop drinking. Without sobriety, all of us are headed for nothing but trouble. Of course the going gets rough at times, but the results are worth the struggle. I know they are in my case."

At Ann's suggestion, Diane began to attend meetings of Al-Anon, where she learned to accept her alcoholic husband as a sick person. But Bob could not seem to accept the reason for his enforced sobriety. He complied with the AA program but continued to be unhappy and uncomfortable at work and at home. Although he seemed to be succeeding in his new job, he often felt insecure. He rationalized that a drink or two might relax his tensions on business trips—"After all, who would know?"—but managed to resist these temptations.

Alex Ross had given him a booklet listing the locations of AA meetings in the various cities where his work took him, but Cutler always found that he was too tired, or too tense, to seek out these contacts. When he was at home, however, he did continue to go to AA meetings at least once a week. Ross had suggested that Cutler do this on his own, without urging either from him or from Diane.

Two years after Bob's promotion, all seemed to be well. He had completed over a year of sobriety; his family life and his business performance progressed. But he was irritable at times and often seemed detached and preoccupied. The truth was that over the previous month he had begun drinking when he was out of town—never more than one or two drinks and always in the privacy of his hotel room, after his day's work was completed. Since he had insomnia at times, his rationalization was that alcohol made him sleep better. His conscience troubled him, but he salved these recurrent twinges with the defense that what he was doing was "for everybody's good."

Over the next few months Bob Cutler almost came to welcome his many necessary trips; he could look forward to his secret drink or two in the evening. He had broken the pattern of sobriety and, when stronger temptation occurred, his defenses were down. One evening at a business dinner, trays of drinks were passed. Cutler took one almost without thinking. After the second, he said to himself, "Oh, well, I'll take a night off."

He really took the night off—as far as his memory was concerned. When he awoke in the morning, he was in a bewildered condition. He had a splitting headache and the clock by his bed told him it was almost midday. Answering a knock on the door, he confronted his firm's Midwestern advertising representative. Within a few minutes he found his gravest fears realized: he had become obnoxiously intoxicated, had engaged in a heated argument with his host over a matter of business, and had been asked to leave. Luckily, his associate had been present and had managed to get him to his hotel room.

Despite Cutler's efforts to placate the associate and his host of the night before, word got back to the home office, and he was put on strict probation. With his job in jeopardy, Cutler continued to resort to alcohol to quell his mounting fears. Before long Diane realized what was happening. This almost overwhelmed her; she had counted so much on her husband's lasting recovery. She tried bravely to convince him to return to AA and sobriety, and for a short while this seemed to work. But about a year and a half after Bob had begun his "limited" drinking, he was brought home one afternoon by an office associate, in a drunken condition.

Diane knew then that she could not continue to endure her husband's drinking one more moment. The next morning, before Bob awoke, she took her two children to her mother's home in a nearby state. She left her husband a note telling him of her decision and suggesting he find living quarters for himself within the next few weeks.

Diane Cutler had used the last resource at her command—she had created a bottom. A week later, Bob lost his job. Because of his continued drinking, his employer reluctantly decided that he was no longer of any use to the firm.

At the moment when everything he valued most in life seemed lost, Bob remembered what he had learned in AA—that alcoholism is not hopeless, provided the alcoholic has a genuine desire to stop drinking. He returned to AA and began to look for a new job. This was not easy to find, as in many places his drinking reputation had preceded him. However, with the help of former associates, he found work with a smaller firm. He frankly told his new employer that he had a drinking problem but was now sober and back in AA.

As time goes on Cutler finds less and less compulsion to drink. He has come to realize that it is easier to stay sober than to get sober. Although he and Diane are still separated, there is hope that they may someday be reunited. They agree that they must both feel certain that the problem has been permanently solved before they again try life together. Meanwhile, both are using as a guide the tested AA slogan, "Easy does it."

* 6

A MAJOR HEALTH PROBLEM

FOR INDUSTRY

American business and industry managements have only recently begun to recognize the magnitude of the problem created by alcoholism among employees. For a long time employers regarded the chronic alcoholic as an irritating but minor problem. Even in 1952, an Opinion Research Corporation survey showed that 84 percent of 433 manufacturing firms did not consider chronic alcoholism a problem among personnel. During the intervening fifteen years, however, there has been a decided change in management thought concerning alcoholism. Among the firms in all areas of the nation's economy which today maintain active company programs on alcoholism are many whose names are widely known.

The Billion-Dollar Hangover

Top management has become increasingly aware that the stage of excessive drinking known as chronic alcoholism is only the end product of a major illness among employees which inflicts heavy operational costs on employers during its entire progression. These costs have been estimated at over $1,000,000,000 annually for United States business and industry. This immense loss has been termed "the billion-dollar hangover," a phrase which has gained general usage since it was first introduced in 1957 in a syndicated series of newspaper articles on the problem of alcoholism in industry.[1]

These are direct costs, primarily resulting from loss of trained manpower, absenteeism, excessive fringe-benefit expense, inefficiency, and above all, poor job performance. There are also many indirect costs traceable to excessive drinking among employees. These include unfortunate public relations on the part of salesmen and other outside employees, the time spent by supervisors in attempting to apply disciplinary measures, extra record-keeping expense, and the general upsetting of company morale.

From the point of view of business and industry, a limited but eminently practical definition of a person suffering from alcoholism is an individual whose repeated or continued over-indulgence interferes with the efficient performance of his work. Contrary to popular belief, only a small part of the progress of alcoholism occurs during the later, chronic stages. The bulk of the illness is now recognized as developing over a period of years. Because many of the sufferers, often described as problem drinkers, are in the early stages of the illness, they constitute an unusually difficult personnel problem. They are found in all types of occupations and despite incipient alcoholism work at their jobs more or less steadily. Their usual pattern of everyday life has not as yet been disrupted but, like their family life, their job performance is showing definite signs of instability.

The University of Utah and Rutgers University were pioneers in presenting courses on alcoholism in industry. Cornell initiated courses beginning in January 1965 through its New York State School of Industrial and Labor Relations. Attendance at these courses on alcoholism in industry is concentrated among operating management and unions. The initial conference for a hand-picked group of line supervisors and medical directors of leading firms was held at the Cornell Club in January 1965, followed by a meeting for personnel managers at the Conference Center of the School of Industrial and Labor Relations in New York City. Follow-up courses for the first group are given annually.

Intensive studies were made of two companies located in the area of Ithaca, New York, site of Cornell, and ideal pilot projects in coping with the problem of alcoholism among personnel were instituted. During the summer months courses are given for union members who act as liaison between union employees and company management. These union people are those who deal directly with the line supervisors in companies, from the president on down through the ranks. In other words, membership in these Cornell courses is drawn from the people in both union and management who deal with the employees directly involved with the operating work of the company. During 1966 the Cornell project conducted fourteen conferences—four for labor union officials, two for industrial medical personnel, two for personnel specialists, and six for various levels of industrial employees.

Between 1959 and 1966 there has been an increase of 50 percent in the number of United States firms which have initiated company programs on alcoholism. An even more striking increase is shown in the number of such firms appearing in the list of the 100 largest United States companies as compiled annually by *Fortune* magazine. Thirty-four of the companies in the 1966 list have alcoholism programs, as compared to four on the 1954 list.

Most of the major life insurance companies now have alcoholism programs for their employees. Furthermore, some of the top companies have taken aggressive steps to acquaint the public with the conception of alcoholism as a treatable disease. Kemper Insurance Company, representing a group of leading casualty and mutual insurance companies, has published full-page advertisements in publications such as *The Wall Street Journal,* as well as in other media, to advise business and industry about this major personnel problem. From its Chicago headquarters, Kemper has widely circulated a pamphlet to management entitled: *A Neglected Area of Loss Reduction; What to Do About the Employee with a Drinking Problem.*[2] The Metropolitan Life Insurance Company of New York has also gone directly to the public through full-page advertisements in *The Reader's Digest* and other high-circulation publications depicting the true and false notions people have concerning alcoholism. These advertisements offered a free copy of the company's booklet, *Alcoholism.*[3]

Outstanding consulting work with United States business and industry is now being done by the Industrial Services Department of the National Council on Alcoholism. In many cases the original contact with individual business firms is made by NCA's Industry Committee, which is composed of top executives from leading companies in several industries. The Industrial Services staff has developed improved techniques for helping companies to study their alcoholism program needs, for more practical definition of the supervisory role, and basic improvements both in early identification of cases and in motivating employees to accept treatment. When tailored to fit individual companies, these approaches enable managements to use an alcoholism program for dealing more effectively with all behavioral-medical problems. The recent trend in these new programs is to include the treatment of alcoholism as a part of the company's general employee health policy.

Speaking at the 27th International Congress on Alcohol and Alcoholism at Frankfurt/Main, Germany, in 1964, R. B. Smithers said:

> The economic loss from alcoholism is primarily in business and industry. . . . The education, prevention, and treatment of alcoholism must become a part of the pivotal, basic institutions of our society. . . . The central position of the business world in the power structure of any industrial nation is clear cut.
>
> Of the more than 25 million alcoholics in the world today, almost half are on company payrolls and only about 7 percent conform to the image of the homeless derelict. Yet the homeless derelict minority remains an obsession out of all proportion to its number and treatment potential. Alcoholism, as an illness, is still closely identified with welfare work, with the persistent notion that only social and welfare agencies are the vehicles for its treatment. Only when business managements and labor unions, large and small, develop realistic policies about alcoholics and follow through on them, will

effective action be taken against this huge public health problem.[4]

By 1968 the concept that alcoholism is an illness has enabled over 200 leading firms to deal constructively with this touchy and costly employee problem. Their practical experiences in working with alcoholic employees combine company health program activities and cooperation with community facilities for referral of employees with a drinking problem—usually those who are in an early- or middle-stage development of the disease.

Less than ten years ago, however, only thirty-four pioneering firms had such programs in effect. To promote the development of further programs in business and industry, the Smithers Foundation in 1959 sent a questionnaire to these companies, asking for suggestions that might be helpful to other companies in setting up their own. Useful material based on their experience was received from Allis-Chalmers Manufacturing Company; American Can Company; American Telephone & Telegraph Company; Bell Telephone of Canada; Caterpillar Tractor Company; Consolidated Edison Company of New York; Corning Glass Works; Detroit Edison Company; Eastman Kodak Company; E. I. du Pont de Nemours & Co.; Endicott Johnson Corporation; Equitable Life Assurance Society of the United States; General Electric Company; General Motors Corporation (Cadillac Division); Hughes Tool Company; Humble Oil and Refining Company; Imperial Oil Company, Ltd.; Ingersoll-Rand Company; Inland Steel Company; International Business Machines Corporation; John Hancock Mutual Life Insurance Company; Kennecott Copper Corporation; Lockheed Aircraft Corporation; Metropolitan Life Insurance Company; New England Telephone and Telegraph Company; New England Electric System; New York Telephone Company; The New York Times; Norton Company; Peoples Gas, Light and Coke Company; Prudential Insurance Company of America; Standard Oil Company of New Jersey; The Texas Company; Western Electric Company. From this material was developed the basic plan which follows.

A Company Program for Dealing with Alcoholism

WHY HAVE A PROGRAM?

Most companies take the position that an employee's drinking is his or her own business, but that doesn't stop the problem drinker from giving management a sizable headache. The National Industrial Conference Board has found that problem drinkers miss work twice as often as other workers and report late more frequently. They have more loss-time accidents, produce less, and make more mistakes.

"Double your best guess at the number of 'worrisome drinkers' in your company for the most likely estimate," H. David Archibald, director of the Alcoholism Research Foundation, Toronto, told a business and industry conference in 1959. The combined experience of the companies which have established alcoholism programs supports this statement. The management's original estimate of the size of the problem of alcoholism among personnel often was doubled and even tripled after a company program had been in operation for a period of time.

The new procedure not only resulted in a greater awareness among supervisors of the symptoms of the disease but also uncovered many "hidden" alcoholics. These employees had previously been shielded from company detection by well-meaning families, family doctors, fellow workers, and even supervisors heretofore fearful of losing valuable employees through dismissal under disciplinary measures. The consensus of company reports concerning programs in operation for two years or more shows that alcoholism affects from 2 percent to 8 percent of these companies' payrolls. In many cases management's original estimate ran from "less than 1 percent" to "not over 2 percent of personnel" at the time of inception of these alcoholism programs.

Seemingly, alcoholism presents a problem to alert management whether a company manufactures cars or processes peanuts. The widespread situation in business and industry was summed up by Dr. John L. Norris, Medical Director, Kodak Park Works,

Eastman Kodak Company, Rochester, N.Y., before a Chicago industrial conference in 1958: "A company that says it doesn't have any problems with alcoholism among its employees today doesn't know what it is talking about."

Awareness of a disturbing problem of alcoholism was expressed in a variety of ways in answers to the request: "Please list the principal factors which guided your decision in initiating your company alcoholism program." Some examples follow:

Allis-Chalmers Manufacturing Company:

> Public relations effect of discharges and the morale effect of unchecked alcoholism on other employees.

Bell Telephone Company of Canada:

> Our previous efforts had been ineffective and led to losses which could be ill afforded by the Company.

Corning Glass Works:

> Lack of information and general "know-how" to cope with this problem.

Eastman Kodak Company:

> We knew in the Medical Department and in the plant that we had a problem and needed help in meeting it.

E. I. du Pont de Nemours & Company:

> Recognition that there was a widespread problem yet the complete failure of the usual sources of help tried up to that time.

Inland Steel Company:

> We wanted to bring our people to the viewpoint that alcoholism is an illness and not a moral question.

International Business Machines Corporation:

> Recognition that with assistance employees afflicted with this disease could make a greater contribution to their fami-

lies, their communities, and the Company, after proper treatment.

Kennecott Copper Company:

High rate of absenteeism among certain employees, humanitarian considerations and the conviction that we ought to give rehabilitation a fair trial before we conclude that the only solution for the problem drinker is discharge.

New England Electric System:

Our Medical Department picked up more and more disability cases due to or aggravated by stages of alcoholism.

New York Telephone Company:

Administrative effort required by supervisors.

The New York Times:

The tendency of supervisors to conceal alcoholics out of loyalty until they were far advanced.

The traditional attitude of most United States employers toward the problem of alcoholism among employees was best summed up some years ago by one nationally known employer: "Oh, we don't have any problems with alcoholics. We fire them." For various reasons, however, this attitude has changed. In this age of automation and electronics skilled workers are not so easily replaced. The companies which have established alcoholism programs regard alcoholics as sick, not weak-willed, individuals. They recognize that many can be rehabilitated and that the company can assist. Their results have been impressive. Some companies report that as many as 70 percent of employees treated have been rehabilitated. These figures are the more noteworthy in that they are reported after a follow-up period of three to five years after original rehabilitation.

However, the surface has hardly been scratched. According to a conservative estimate made by the National Council on

Alcoholism, business and industry employ at least 3,000,000 sufferers from alcoholism whose out-of-control drinking keeps them off the job a total of 36,000,000 workdays a year. In addition, millions of abnormally heavy drinkers drag through millions of unproductive hangover days as "half men" (a term applied originally to such employees by the Yale Center of Alcohol Studies). These employees alienate customers, make serious mistakes, are prone to accidents. Worst of all, their drinking is likely to lead to advanced stages of alcoholism.

The decision of pioneering companies to try to deal constructively with the employee with a drinking problem was influenced by two factors: the work of Alcoholics Anonymous in effecting rehabilitation, and the American Medical Association's decision that alcoholism is a disease, which brought this ancient moral and social problem over into the less controversial field of public health.

It is important, however, to take into account the unique features of this illness. Unlike other diseases, alcoholism produces deceptive defenses, which allow the alcoholic worker to keep on drinking despite the severe damage his drinking does to job performance. Before he will change, some meaningful crisis must cut through these defenses. He must be brought to a realization that his job security and the economic well-being of his family and himself depend on his rehabilitation from his present drinking problems.

As a disease, alcoholism could safely be approached by business and industrial management. The pioneers in the experiment formed company procedures which offered a program of personal treatment for employees under company sponsorship. Previously the fear of detection and possible dismissal had kept many alcoholic employees from doing anything about their problem, even if they had known where to go for help.

Dr. George N. Gehrmann, as Medical Director of E. I. du-Pont de Nemours & Company, was one of the first industrial leaders to perceive this constructive possibility. Now retired, he said in retrospect:

Alcoholics were not then, nor are now, more numerous in the duPont Company than in the community at large but we did recognize a widespread serious problem. We saw a need to retain valuable and experienced personnel in both supervision and the work level who suffered from this treatable disease.

The results of industrial programs in effecting long-term rehabilitation of alcoholic employees have been remarkably good over a period of years compared with results observed in treatment of other groups of alcoholics drawn from the general public. One cause undoubtedly is the fact that employees who have been able to maintain many years of employment at the same company tend as a group to be relatively more stable. In addition, they are likely to be better motivated for treatment and abstinence by the possibility of losing valued jobs and company benefits.

CONSTRUCTIVE COERCION

Because the work place is typically organized around *authority*, the definition of alcoholism can be given to any alcoholic employee in an atmosphere of "constructive coercion." To a simple, easily understood definition can be tied an inevitable result of continued alcoholism: the loss of the job.

Applied in an impersonal fashion, but underscoring as its main feature a positive offer of treatment help, this sanction is probably the most readily available way for getting the developing alcoholic to face up to his problem. Obviously such use of authority must be tailored to specific cases. Also obvious is the fact that this approach is not a cure-all, but compared to possible action by home or church it probably has more teeth in it. So it must be ranked very high among available tools. In short, an effective approach to the problem of alcoholism calls for the development of new, authoritative group sanctions. In our society, job-centered definitions, treatment, and sanctions offer an excellent source for these needed forces.

Work, and the work place, continue to play an important role for Americans, especially men. Despite a widespread reduction in the skill content of the job, it still occupies a central position in our lives. In a recent national sample, 80 percent of adult men said they would continue to work even if they could get along easily without working. Retirement often brings with it a sense of loss at no longer performing a job. This feeling occurs among employees in a wide range of occupations. Unemployment has demoralizing effects beyond the financial problems involved.

Today there are also increased economic benefits in the job. "Fringes" of every conceivable kind have been added to the cash incomes of millions of jobs. Seniority due to union membership adds a second economic investment. It represents in the minds of many employees a degree of job ownership, something like home ownership after years of mortgage payments.

While the emotional and economic values of jobs remain high, so does the work routine and discipline that organizes them. Thus in manufacturing and retail trades the number of planners, supervisors, schedulers, and coordinators is growing. On large numbers of jobs the timing and sequence of tasks has never been so specifically spelled out for the employee. Not only does the typical employee have many investments in the job; he usually does his job in a network of controls and routines which make his work behavior highly visible to bosses and fellow workers.

A developing alcoholic is therefore usually unable to disregard a job threat, particularly when constructive chances for treatment are associated with the threat. He knows that the results of his alcoholism can be seen and defined. For once in the progress of his illness, he faces a situation he cannot manipulate or stall. Many potential behavior problems are held in check by such firm, easily understood social pressures, even though there is still some emotional crippling as a result.

Finally, such sanctions and the treatment offer linked to them can reach a mass of developing alcoholics provided there is widespread acceptance by industry and business. Compared with such agencies as welfare and social services, the work world can influence and educate literally millions.

The greatest intangible reward for the company from a successful alcoholism program has been found in the retention of valued employees. Statistics show that the average alcoholic revealed through a company program was found in the middle grade. He is usually a skilled or semiskilled person, ranging in age between thirty-five and fifty, has been at least seven years with his company, is married, maintains his own home, and usually has two or more children. In other words, he is a responsible member of the community. (See Appendix C.)

The average experience of companies with effective programs shows that the rate of long-term recovery for alcoholic employees, after initial rehabilitation, is over 50 percent of those accepting treatment.

ORGANIZING THE PROGRAM

The word program sometimes suggests a massive undertaking to managements preoccupied with many other problems. To attempt to study company programs already in operation and adapt one of them to an individual company's needs is usually ineffective. But when executives study the problem clearsightedly and consider ways of meeting it within their established management-employee relationships, they find that to help alcoholic employees for both their own welfare and that of the company, an informal program may be launched with a minimum of organizational change and with existent facilities.

Supervisors are briefed on the symptoms and nature of alcoholic progression and on ways and means of handling this problem among the employees under their direction. This information is readily available from the handbooks for supervisors issued by companies already experienced in maintaining alcoholism programs (see Selected Reading List).

The management instructs its supervisory employees to bring all apparent cases of behavioral-medical problems to the medical department for diagnosis. If the diagnosis is indeed alcoholism, in one of the various degrees of the illness, referral is made by the medical department to available community resources. This is an alcoholism program in its simplest form and dozens of companies have at least taken their first action on the problem in this manner.

However, there is one important requisite for any successful effort of this nature. Management must let it be known to everyone concerned within the company's organization that this is a management decision and one that management stands solidly behind. Usually the new policy concerning alcoholism is made known to all personnel down to the supervisory level. In many instances, it is circulated among the employees themselves through various internal communication channels—company house organs, meetings of employee committees, through the cooperation of union representatives, and other means of contact.

The reason that a company program to combat problem drinking, or its later more virulent forms of the illness, must be originated, sold all down the line, and carried out by management is that confidence is the keynote of success in the execution of such a program. The employees must be convinced that management means what it says—that disclosure of the nature of the illness, either voluntarily or through supervisory action, will not result in dismissal. This fear has been built up over many past years of disciplinary treatment and is not easily dispelled.

As R. Harris, Jr., an executive of the International Business Machines Corporation, has pointed out: "Management (by this move) shows recognition that with assistance employees afflicted with this disease can—after treatment—make a greater contribution to their families, their communities, and the company."

In formulating a company policy, four points are basic:

1. That top management define alcoholism among its employees as a health problem requiring therapy.

2. That the company take a treatment attitude toward this health problem, offering assistance in securing therapy.

3. That it be clearly understood that after a reasonable opportunity for progress, the employee will be dismissed unless there is noticeable improvement in work.

4. That this policy be communicated widely by company officers with their full approval.

Naturally any individual company will tailor these points to its own particular situation and conditions. Current company programs show a wide variety of ways of expressing them. These four points are, however, essential to a constructive policy toward the difficult personnel problem of alcoholism.

ONE COMPANY'S FORMULATION OF POLICY

The following statement of company policy was prepared in 1951 for the Bell Telephone Company of Canada, after management discussions, by the Medical Director, Dr. W. D. Cruickshank. The entire problem was approached and set forth to supervisory employees with such clarity that little further action was needed except the implementation of the program as outlined.

At a recent meeting of the Employees' Benefit Committee further consideration was given to the development of a company policy with respect to the management of the problem of alcoholism within the employee group. Particular attention was given by the Committee to the question of eligibility to Sickness Disability Benefits and Disability Pension and its decision in regard to these items is covered in the following recommendation.

The Committee has seen fit to consider alcoholism as a health problem and has recommended the adoption of the following policy which the departments had previously reviewed and approved of in principle:

1. That it be recognized that most cases of alcoholism or "problem drinking" present a health problem.

2. That each case of incipient or suspected alcoholism or "problem drinking" be encouraged to seek adequate medical investigation and advice without delay.

3. That each case involving a health problem be considered eligible for Sickness Disability Benefits or Disability Pension under the Company's Plan for Employees' Pensions and Disability Benefits, if the condition is sufficiently advanced to produce disablement from work.

4. That where possible *final* disciplinary action in cases of alcoholism be delayed until health factors have been adequately reviewed and treatment undertaken without success.

"Problem drinking" or alcoholism is a public health problem of major and probably increasing concern to most communities and industries. It ranks within the first four of the major public health problems on this continent at the present time.

Although the extent to which the problem in this Company affects productivity, sickness absence or accident frequency is at this stage unknown, experience indicates that a problem does exist. Carefully done surveys elsewhere have indicated that about 3 percent of industrial workers are "problem drinkers."

"Problem drinking" is considered to exist for the individual worker:

(*a*) when his (or her) work is materially reduced in efficiency and dependability in large part because of drinking, and

(*b*) when such drinking is not an isolated experience but is more or less repetitive, and

(*c*) when such drinking results in recognizable interference with health or personal relations.

It is only within quite recent years that a public health approach to the problem of alcoholism has been undertaken. The disciplinary approach prompted largely on moral grounds has been traditionally used, with limited success, as has been the case with many other diseases having social implications. This trend to consider alcohol as a health problem and to bring it out into the open where it can be discussed freely and where problem cases can be referred in the early stages when treatment and rehabilitation can be most profitably undertaken is encouraging. While it is true that few communities are adequately equipped to deal effectively with the problem, many communities are, at the present time, attempting to improve the facilities available for the treatment of alcoholism. Much, however, can be accomplished by the effective use of existing facilities.

The Medical Department is anxious to be of all possible assistance to supervision in helping to point up cases and to assist in planning treatment and rehabilitation programs for those cases that are discovered. It is also prepared to be of any possible assistance to departments in developing the case-finding skills of supervisory people. In the meantime it would be desirable to encourage supervisors to bring known or suspected cases to the Medical Department for diagnosis and recommendations. In referring cases of problem drinking to the Medical Department it is important that the reason for referral be discussed in detail with the patient and with the physician prior to medical investigation. The success of any program within industry directed to the early diagnosis of alcoholism will, of necessity, depend largely on the degree of interest shown by supervisors in the problem and also on the ability of supervisors to bring problem drinkers or potential problem drinkers for assistance in relation to their health problem.

Under present conditions a good deal can be offered to the alcoholic in the way of treatment and rehabilitation services. Alcoholism is by no means a hopeless condition.

REHABILITATION MEASURES

The facilities for treating alcoholic employees within a plant are usually restricted to the services of a company's medical department. Business and industry should not be expected to provide complete facilities for the rehabilitation of alcoholics (or for other sick employees). However, as the National Industrial Conference Board has pointed out,[5] companies can help by identifying those in their employ that need attention, and referring them to the resources and facilities offered by the community. The identification of early cases, of course, offers the most promise for all concerned. The NICB also suggests that companies should support these community centers that work with alcoholics.

A community resource for rehabilitation listed by the NICB is the National Council on Alcoholism which has local affiliates in more than eighty communities across the country, in which physicians, scientists, and laymen work together. The NCA, formerly supported almost entirely by individuals and foundations, is beginning to receive financial aid from industry as well.

Community facilities vary in different parts of the United States, although their prevalence has been steadily increasing. More than forty state governments have established state commissions and agencies for combating alcoholism. Some of these state agencies maintain area facilities for the treatment and rehabilitation of alcoholics. Other state programs contribute to the support of outside facilities which are available for consultation, treatment, and other services. However, there is a national need for more expanded state facilities.

Seriously ill alcoholic employees may require short-term hospitalization. Today more and more doctors and hospitals are treating alcoholism as a distinct illness. Over 3,000 general hospitals now accept alcoholics as patients. Any local medical association will know which local hospitals do so. Many county and state medical associations have subcommittees on alcoholism and many of these groups have brought pressure on local hospitals to offer specialized treatment for alcoholic patients.

When a company is considering setting up a program on alcoholism, the management may wonder whether such a move will place too heavy a load on the company's medical department or necessitate enlarging the medical staff. According to the Reverend Yvelin Gardner, Deputy Executive Director of the National Council on Alcoholism, "An alcoholism program in a company does not mean adding to the medical staff. It really reduces its load. Less time is spent in the aggregate on alcoholics with such a program than when there is none at all."

COMPANIES AS COMMUNITY LEADERS

Where community agencies for rehabilitation of alcoholics are lacking, companies concerned with the problem may be able to initiate joint action to provide them. In a number of instances during the past fifteen years individual business or industrial firms have been leaders in a concerted community movement for better community education in the problem of alcoholism and the expansion of facilities to take care of the rehabilitation of alcoholics.

In Rochester, New York, Eastman Kodak Company was a prime mover in initiating an active program of public education concerning alcoholism which resulted in the formation of clinics for the care of patients, and increased understanding of the problem by the medical profession through these clinics which were under direct community supervision.

Corning Glass Works' participation in a similar project in upper New York State was described by the company's medical director, Dr. D. E. Billman, as follows:

A meeting of interested community leaders and industrial people resulted in the formation of the Corning Area Committee on Alcoholism. The new Committee was backed financially by industry—including Ingersoll-Rand Company, ourselves, and other interested companies—to enable it to get off the ground.

The Committee operates an Alcoholism Information Center in the Corning Hospital. Our medical and insurance programs within our company handle alcoholism in the same fashion as any other disease and our in-plant program cooperates fully with community facilities outside.

The local Alcoholics Anonymous groups have been interested and helpful in initiating the program as well as rendering immeasurable help in the disposition and therapy of cases. The community program has received the financial support of the United Fund and has made tremendous progress in educating the various community groups. There has been a reciprocal interest and activity in the respective groups in this subtle disease which has and will continue to reduce the morbidity and mortality in our industries and the community.

Consolidated Edison Company of New York in 1952 spent $25,000 to help set up a consultation clinic for alcoholism at New York University-Bellevue Medical Center. The clinic was the first in this country to be devoted solely to the alcoholic in industry. Some twenty other companies in the New York metropolitan area, including Bell Telephone Laboratories and Metropolitan Life Insurance Company, now regularly refer employees with a drinking problem to the clinic.

COSTS TO THE COMPANY

Although the cost of the New York City clinic, originally financed by Consolidated Edison, might discourage interested management, the reports of dozens of companies now maintaining programs agree that the cost of supporting a program, while difficult to separate from the general budget of the medical department, is minimal. A typical comment is: "We save the individual cost of treatment many times over in a multitude of ways." No notable rise in medical department costs has been reported, and the industrial physicians engaged in in-plant work report that, if anything, there has been a decrease in treating other employee ailments "formerly ascribed to everything else but drinking."

Few companies can or care to make specific estimates of their alcoholism program's annual cost, but all are enthusiastic about the program's continuance. Actual figures, however, were supplied by Allis-Chalmers Manufacturing Company, which a few years ago estimated that its alcoholism program was saving the company some $80,000 yearly just in reducing absenteeism. Among workers who have been treated under the program, the absentee rate has been slashed from 8 to 3 percent. The firing rate for problem drinkers has been cut from 95 percent to 8 percent during that period.

THE SUPERVISOR AS KEY MAN

All companies operating alcoholism programs point out the importance of supervisors or foremen in the success of the operation. At least in the beginning, very few employees will come forward voluntarily and state that they have a drinking problem, although many companies report that this may occur as the program becomes more generally recognized and employees gain confidence in management's stand.

Certainly no efficient supervisor wants to be suspected of snooping or interfering in the private lives of his employees. Therefore he must be trained to observe work performance and to recognize and report any changing behavioral-medical problem including alcoholism.

It would be most desirable to identify developing alcoholics in the very earliest stages of their illness, but this is usually impossible because their symptoms are inconspicuous in a usual drinking environment. Certain signs, however, appear at the time when the alcoholic is most likely to respond to therapy—about the early middle phases.

The table on page 158, prepared by Professor Harrison M. Trice, shows the nature of these signs and compares reports of what supervisors of alcoholics have reported as clues.[6] Supervisors were especially aware of these clues that relate to a busy supervisor's workday—for example, leaving the post temporarily and lower quality of work. Alcoholics themselves describe similar clues. The only difference is that alcoholics describe as the earliest clues very private things that happened inside themselves and could not be seen by an active busy boss.

Frequency of Signs of Developing Alcoholism As Reported
by Supervisors of Alcoholics and Alcoholics Themselves

TYPE	SUPERVISORS	ALCOHOLICS

I
Noticed early
and frequently
thereafter
	Leaving post temporarily
	Absenteeism: half day or
	  day
	More unusual excuses for
	  absences
	Lower quality of work
	Mood changes after lunch
	Red or bleary eyes
		Hangover on job
		Increased nervousness /
		  jitteryness
		Hand tremors

II Noticed later but frequently thereafter	Less even, more spas- modic work pace Lower quality of work Hangovers on job	Red or bleary eyes More edgy / irritable Avoiding boss or associates

III
Noticed fairly
early but in-
frequently
thereafter
	Loud talking
	Drinking at lunch time
	Longer lunch periods
	Hand tremors
		Morning drinking before
		  work
		Drinking at lunch time
		Drinking during working
		  hours
		Absenteeism: half day or
		  day
		More unusual excuses for
		  absences
		Leaving post temporarily
		Leaving work early
		Late to work

IV
Noticed late
and infre-
quently there-
after
	Drinking during working
	  hours
	Avoiding boss or associ-
	  ates
	Flushed face
	Increase in real minor
	  illnesses
		Mood changes after lunch
		Longer lunch periods
		Breath purifiers
		Lower quality of work
		Lower quantity of work

Medical staffs in many of the companies mention two important clues they have found indicative of a possible drinking problem. These are domestic or financial difficulties.

In another study [7] Professor Trice has described many clues discovered by supervisors in locating problem drinkers in the early stages of their illness. Some of these are:

> The employee's usual failure to report his inability to get to the job. At first a member of his family reports his absence before it takes place. Later in his illness, his absence just happens without any advance indication. . . .
>
> Sales executives and salesmen who "must drink with customers to do business." Supervisors who "have to drink with their tough workmen to keep them working." . . .
>
> The problem drinker who devotes much of his time and energy to getting through the workday without drinking or in covering up the fact that he is drinking during working hours.

An excellent booklet for the guidance of supervisors has been prepared by the Western Electric Company.[8] Written in simple language and drawn from actual experience, it should be of immense help to the supervisor or foreman upon whose judgment so much of the effectiveness of a company's program on alcoholism depends. (See Selected Reading List.)

THE MEDICAL DEPARTMENT

"The physician in industry is in a key position to discern the occupational features of alcoholism. He is also in a notably advantageous position to help motivate the alcoholic to seek assistance," says Dr. Arnold Z. Pfeffer, formerly in charge of the Consultation Clinic for Alcoholism, New York University-Bellevue Medical Center.[9]

Dr. John L. Norris of Eastman Kodak Company has said:

In a subject of this magnitude, it is completely impossible to impose a formal detailed program on any industry or any specific company. However there is a common denominator which seems to be present in all effective industrial programs of which I have any knowledge. This is a careful use of authority to insure acceptance on the part of the individual sufferer that he has a problem, to the point where he will at least take treatment for a long enough period of time to receive the benefits of what medicine and community education have to give.[10]

In smaller companies the industrial nurse often carries out medical tasks. She is uniquely placed to do a job of early identification and referral. "Often developing alcoholics will confide in her and listen to her advice," points out Professor Trice. "Furthermore, for practical-minded supervisors, she is less representative of authoritative management and they will come to her more naturally about their alcoholic employees."[11]

Unions and Alcoholism Programs

The control of alcoholism, both within a company and in a community, represents an area in which management and unions can work together to the benefit of all concerned when the situation is properly viewed as a problem affecting both.

When a unionized company undertakes an alcoholism program, its effectiveness will be tremendously increased by securing the union's cooperation. The best results are obtained when this is done before and during the official launching. This does not mean that the company need include the union in its original decision to develop a policy, but that union officials should be told the nature of the policy to permit discussion and explanation. Management has a real right to formulate a program on alcoholism and administer it as it sees fit. Decisions by the National Labor Relations Board have established that management does not have to tolerate an alcoholic employee, and this has been recognized in the grievance procedure. But the combined weight of both union and management is obviously more effective than management alone. A hostile union can cripple the practical operation of a policy if it has a false notion of it.

By insisting on its legal position, management will merely defeat the treatment purpose of its policy. A far better approach is to understand how the union tends to react and to present the policy within that framework. The traditional role of the union is to protect its members against alleged unfair treatment. Members expect it to perform this function, so it does. But usually union officials fulfill this role, where alcoholism cases are concerned, on an informal basis, avoiding formal grievance procedures if possible. They perform the protective function without taking a specific case too far. When an alcoholic employee has to be dismissed under the new policy, if management keeps the negotiations at this level, the union can go through its defense of the case without taking a firm stand as it would have to do if the case went to the grievance procedure. Once there the union will be fully committed to defense, claiming insufficient warning, poor diagnosis, or no measure for alleged poor performance of work. In short, rarely is anything of a therapeutic nature gained by "going formal."

Naturally the union wants to feel that it has a part in the new alcoholism policy. Its representatives want to be able to tell the alcoholic member that they can help him get treatment and "another chance." Local union officials are often aware of the problem and realize the futility of defending the problem drinker. But they also need an opportunity to be identified with the policy, to claim cooperation and inclusion. In such cases they often tend to adopt a participating role. They can appreciate the nature of the illness, the increased effect if there is cooperation, the need for clear job sanctions in case of poor progress. The shop steward often shares with the supervisor the headache of a problem drinker. Fellow workers often make their resentment of him known to the union steward.

Management can more effectively develop and institute its

policy if it will recognize the need of the union to be informed of developments and to be identified with them. If the union is informally prepared for a policy, and if management understands the union's need informally to perform a protective function, management's prerogatives can be fully recognized without arousing union resistance. In such an atmosphere it is much easier to explain that the "salvage of some means the firing of some," based on individual assessment. This is probably the most difficult practical point for unions to accept. They are much more likely to do so if they have had an opportunity to be identified with the policy at an early stage of its writing. If there happen to be members of Alcoholics Anonymous among the union officials and they offer their help, they can be very effective in developing acceptance of the kind of company alcoholism policy that was described in the previous section.

In a survey of alcoholism in industry, Leo Perlis, director of National AFL-CIO Community Service Activities, has suggested some of the ways in which organized labor and business and industrial management can and should work together to combat alcoholism and rehabilitate alcoholics. Excerpts from this survey [12] follow:

> Labor and management must recognize the fact that the alcoholic needs competent help. We must learn about existing community facilities, and we must help establish facilities where none exist. . . . The union itself has a singular responsibility to help all its members by helping its alcoholic members. Certainly, alcoholics hurt not only themselves but everybody about them, including our social and economic fabric. Companies, too, can help, through non-controversial, non-collective-bargaining committees of union and management representatives, to establish liaison with the proper community agencies for the purpose of providing essential services to the alcoholic and his family during the entire period of treatment. Such committees might very well include the medical director, the nurse, and union counselors. . . .

Alcoholism in industry . . . is a problem that calls for earnest study by both management and labor, for both of us are intimately involved in the situation that arises from problem drinkers. In far too many cases, management has attempted to ignore labor in dealing with this problem. They have felt that the handling of problem drinkers was a prerogative of management. On the other hand, labor has just as often refused to face up to the facts—has arbitrarily defended the problem drinker without regard to the fact that sheltering him is a disservice.

The experiences that labor and management have had in the broad field of social work should be used as guideposts in alcoholism. . . . At the community level, we have been able to stress areas of mutuality of interest rather than conflict. We have sought jointly to improve health, welfare and recreational services for the betterment of all of us. While the problem drinker is an in-plant rather than an out-of-plant matter, it is still essentially a social responsibility that calls for the same approach that has proven so successful and so rewarding in our community relationships. Certainly, it calls for a program worked out jointly between management and labor—a program to which both parties can give their unqualified support.

* 7

ALCOHOL EDUCATION:

SOME SIGNIFICANT AREAS

A prominent physician has remarked that if alcoholism were a communicable disease, a state of national emergency would be declared. It is partly communicable, because families and associates, through lack of knowledge, contribute to its spread. Education may be considered a vaccine for reducing the annually increasing prevalence of alcoholism among the peoples of various countries. However, for real effectiveness, everyone must be educated about this complex illness.

Recently there has been an increase of public interest regarding the problem of alcoholism among women. Although it has long been recognized, particularly among members of Alcoholics Anonymous, that there is a high proportion of women among our total alcoholic population, modern alcohol education has brought this fact more clearly into the view of the general public. This has had its beneficial effects. Since the stigma of alcoholism has been lessened, women in business and industry are increasingly coming forward for treatment through company programs. The publicity regarding warning signals of possible alcoholism has given to many housewives, and to others engaged in occupations of a more or less private nature, the courage to do something constructive about their condition.

Alcoholism is the only major illness in which the educated layman can be of invaluable aid in diagnosis and treatment. The early warning signs are usually of a behavioral nature, so that the doctor is really not needed at this stage of the illness. As with cancer, early detection is vital but difficult. There are practically no outward physical signs and little pain. One of the most confusing aspects of alcoholism is that it shows up in so many forms. It can also be likened to cancer in that there are many different species. In its early stages, with some alcoholics, alcoholism is a physical illness; with others, a mental illness; and with a third group, behavioral. At a later stage the illness shows symptoms of all three types. In the beginning, therefore, only one discipline may be needed to effect recovery.

The concept of alcoholism as an illness has proved to have practical value in motivating people to learn about one of the greatest health problems in the world today. More national and community education programs are urgently needed. So are guidelines for effective education in the schools—secondary schools, colleges, and graduate schools of law, social work, and medicine. As the earlier chapters of this book have shown, further extensive research is required on all aspects of the disease.

The crux of the entire problem of combating alcoholism lies in the effectiveness of the program for public education about the true nature of the disease.[1] This chapter includes reports of pioneer educational efforts in three important areas: in the secondary schools; among public health nurses; and toward the acceptance and proper treatment of alcoholic patients by hospital managements and personnel.

The Secondary Schools

Since drinking is an accepted social custom among the majority of American adults young people are being increasingly exposed to alcohol with the danger that the prevalence of alcoholism will increase. Statistics indicate that of 300,000 known alcoholics in New York City, about 1 percent are between the ages of fifteen and nineteen.

The only real prevention of the spread of this disease lies in education about its nature and effects in the secondary schools and colleges. Young people must be taught what alcohol is, what its potentials are, and the risks involved in using it. They must be taught that alcohol, unless used in moderation, is a drug which has definite effects that can be habit-forming, as well as addictive. Realistic health education about drinking, including the warning signs of possible alcoholism, can produce in sensible young people an early recognition of their possible sensitivity to alcohol.

Today every state in the United States requires that some education on alcohol and its usage be given in the public high schools, but few of the private secondary schools have such a program. The idea that systematic education on alcohol problems should be a permanent, on-going part of the curriculum in these schools led to a symposium for representatives of forty-five schools.[2] Excerpts from some of the symposium speeches follow.

Raymond G. McCarthy, Associate Professor of Health Education, Yale University Center of Alcohol Studies [now deceased]:

Alcohol problems in general, including the role alcohol plays in the lives of our teen-agers, do not arise from any single factor, nor are they amenable to unilateral solution. Many authorities reflect different viewpoints regarding the use of beverage alcohol in this society. A school administrator or faculty member may express dissatisfaction with the responsibility placed upon the school in respect to alcohol education, feeling that this belongs properly with the family or church. . . .

We are not sure what teen-agers think about alcohol, or even what their real "alcoholic behavior" is, and we must find out if an improved approach to instruction in the classroom is to be undertaken. In a survey of students in one community, 64 percent "drank socially" and only 14 percent were total abstainers. We must recognize adolescent needs in respect to alcohol education, rather than predicating our programs upon an adult frame of reference. The schools have a responsibility to interpret the society in which their students are to function and if the use of alcohol is an unresolved issue, we must explore constructive attitudes—with the transmittal of sounder attitudes to succeeding generations of young people.

Dr. Mitchell Gratwick, Headmaster, Horace Mann School, New York, N.Y.:

Excessive drinking is not a problem in the high schools, except in isolated instances. But parents frequently look to the schools for help with their children in many areas, including alcohol. The schools cannot involve themselves in all these problems, but they cannot summarily reject such pleas for help. Where students are not informed by their parents, the church, or their doctors, an additional burden is placed on the school, but it should accept this as an opportunity.

Our extracurricular educational efforts in these areas are still experimental and we will appreciate any help that we can get in improving education in the field of alcohol. Our policy is to present the facts and allow the individual to choose the facts that he thinks are important to him. Some individual help to students by way of guidance and counseling by an adviser is given as an extracurricular responsibility.

In the ninth grade general science course we devote a month to health education, of which three to four days are devoted to alcohol studies. There is no satisfactory text—simply informal talks, lectures, newspaper articles, and an occasional visiting speaker from AA. This is *not* the way to do it. It should be integrated into some kind of whole, as a part of an extracurricular program. One student suggested that a series of lectures could be easily integrated into the science curriculum—just as in the driver-training course the effect of alcohol on reflexes and so forth is included, with good practical results on drinking behavior while driving. A school questionnaire, answers to which are confidential, showed that alcohol education in the schools should be undertaken concurrently with learning the drinking habits of the parents themselves; their attitudes toward their own and their children's drinking; the relevance of religious background and customs; the actual drinking habits of the children themselves and their motivations for drinking; and the attitudes of the peer group as well as other groups.

Clifford R. Brownell, Chairman of the Department of Health, Physical Education, and Recreation, Teachers College, Columbia University:

Public health education is defined as the health education of the general public. There is a need for cooperative efforts among educational institutions, public health organizations, and voluntary agencies concerned primarily with this problem. The question of alcohol education in the secondary schools has two aspects: legal (state laws and regulations of education departments requiring same) and moral, dealing with the general welfare of citizens beyond legal enactments—the "right thing" to do—and usually moral responsibility comes first, followed by statutory revisions. Instruction on alcohol often comes under health education, but moral persuasion usually dictates the emphasis that is given.

Instruction normally follows one of three directives: (1) comply with the legal directive which sets a minimum time for the subject; (2) go beyond minimum standards; (3) favor instruction about traditional subjects to the disadvantage of alcohol education. The alarming threat of increased consumption of alcoholic beverages by citizens and potential effects of this threat in undermining morals, opportunity, and security of youth indicates clearly the imperative need for more and better education about the subject. Strong programs of public health education have been established in recent years but the cooperation and support of schools and voluntary agencies is needed.

Education about alcohol deserves a prominent place in the school curriculum. Education is viewed as a process for the development of proper attitudes, habits, knowledges, and skills that involve experiences of greatest value now, and to prepare youth for later happiness and success—"to live most and serve best." Emphasis on academic achievement seems to be running too far ahead of subject matter designed to make human beings better able to cope with problems associated with wholesome personal and family living and responsible citizenry.

The social history of this country reveals a willingness by the people to attack vigorously any force that threatens the welfare of its composite citizenry. Once the people have become alerted and informed they will act. Schools represent a first line of defense against the great social threat of alcoholism. No agency is so well equipped as the schools to provide effective leadership in dealing with the problem of alcohol education among children and youth. Neither the home nor the church can do the job alone. The facts are readily available from various education and health authorities and voluntary agencies, in the form of pamphlets and audio-visual materials. Expert help can be provided.

Over the years, private schools have set the pace in education and have enjoyed a position of prominence in the minds of the general public. This challenge applies both to the quality of the instruction given and also to meeting the needs of a changing culture. The hope that private education will continue to look ahead and provide leadership in matters of the social good means a hard look at and a positive approach to the need for stepped-up programs in education about alcohol in private schools.

Mrs. Vashti I. Cain, Supervisor, Narcotics Education, Mississippi State Department of Education:

There is no blueprint for developing programs of alcohol education. It varies with states, communities, and schools. In 1938 the Mississippi Legislature passed a law authorizing the State Department of Education to employ a supervisor for teaching the effects of alcohol, narcotics, and other habit-forming drugs. This was to be taught in all grades of the public schools, and the state colleges and institutions were authorized, in their discretion, to cooperate with the supervisor in carrying out this program. . . . Most young people are eager to learn about all aspects of growing up. Their need to know about alcohol and alcoholism is a real one. The schools have the responsibility to provide this instruction for the students. Aspects of alcohol education that demand special consideration are the social, cultural, and religious conflicts which are involved.

The Mississippi law does not give specifics regarding contents and context of instruction. The program has been activated through a four-fold program: (1) informal adult education; (2) teacher education; (3) teaching aids; (4) consultative services. There is no formal adult education in the state and efforts in this area are channeled through community, civic, and lay professional groups, including local committees on alcoholism. Through radio, television, current periodicals, and newspaper articles other adult citizens are reached. Some problems of the public schools are: creating interest and cooperation between faculty and community; adjusting the crowded curriculum; and selecting teachers who are prepared to offer instruction about alcohol and alcoholism.

The teacher is the key to any program of instruction. Her function is to instill a freedom of approach to facts and ideas which will assist students in making adjustments that are based on realistic examination of conditions and possible consequences. Teachers must have the opportunity to evaluate their own attitudes and to become familiar with recent findings. Educational opportunities are offered to teachers on an in-service and pre-service basis. For the pre-service teachers, four senior colleges offer accredited courses and nine junior and senior colleges correlate units in alcohol education with related subjects. For in-service teachers, a limited number of opportunities have been developed. Each year, at least one Mississippi teacher attends the Yale School [of Alcoholic Studies; now at Rutgers]. Since 1952, many teachers have enrolled in the Mississippi Summer School of Alcohol Studies.

Supplementary teaching aids have been provided in the form of bulletins. Starting in 1947 a unit outline on alcoholism was included in a manual for teaching health in the public schools. Later the outline was developed in narrative form and this has been used by both students and teachers. The *Alcohol Education Handbook* [see Selected Reading List] was designed at the request of administrators and teachers to assist in the organization of programs of alcohol education. The Mississippi Audio-Visual Department makes available films, filmstrips, and records to the schools. Teachers and librarians are also alerted to national publications, organizations, and other community resources.

Consultative services are available to administrators, teachers, state and private agencies, professional organizations, and church groups.

Dr. W. K. Ferrier, Educational Director of the Oregon Alcohol Education Committee:

In Oregon, a committee of five members is appointed by the governor. This committee, known as the Oregon Alcohol Education Committee, is a division of the Oregon Liquor Control Commission. Oregon is one of eighteen states which exercise control over alcoholic beverages through a state monopoly plan.

Under the law, the committee has two specific functions: (1) to promote a program of education about alcohol problems and alcoholism; (2) to develop and support clinics for the treatment of alcoholism and problem drinking.

The committee considers the education of teachers about the problems of alcohol and alcoholism to be of prime importance. Through the cooperation of the Oregon State System of Higher Education, a course known as Alcohol Studies in the School Curriculum has been offered to teachers and others throughout the state for the past eleven years. This course carries three hours of undergraduate or graduate credit at the college level and is offered under the auspices of the General Extension Division.

In addition to teacher education, conferences for professional groups and lay people have been presented. These have included special conferences or workshops for physicians, clergymen, social workers, nurses, parole officers and law enforcement personnel.

A third feature of the program includes consulting services to secondary schools and to colleges. These services consist of providing advice and guidance to teachers and administrators who wish to develop a program of alcohol education in the schools. A library of current objective literature is provided for each school room or class. These libraries are lent for the duration of the program. Films, filmstrips, and other audio-visual aids are lent to the school free of charge. The State of Oregon has developed a manual for teachers, *Alcohol Education in Oregon Public Schools* [see Selected Reading List]. This was printed in 1956 and approximately 16,000 copies were distributed. A workshop group of secondary teachers in 1958 prepared a *Resource Unit on Alcohol Studies*, of which 500 copies were distributed.

When we are invited by a school or college to assist in developing a program of alcohol education, we schedule a conference with teachers and administrators. We acquaint them with the literature available and the services which the State of Oregon can provide. We also arrange to return to the school as consultants in the class room if the teacher desires. We do not attempt to usurp the responsibility of the teacher and teach the class. We try to make it clear that we are serving as consultants. We often assist students in finding information or preparing a report. Occasionally we are called upon to answer questions which the teacher refers to us.

We feel that the best method of teaching about alcohol problems has been to integrate the material into existent curricula. Such a unit can be included in courses relating to health, mental hygiene, biological science, social studies, driver education and home economics.

We have found that the most desirable length of time to be spent on a unit on alcohol problems varies from one to four weeks. The majority of the teachers who have completed our evaluation sheet feel that two weeks is the minimum and three or four weeks would be more desirable.

Every effort is made by the consultants to stress the fact that students must make their own decisions. Our role and that of the teacher is to supply them with information and give them an opportunity for research and discussion. We emphasize to the teacher the importance of developing and maintaining an objective, unbiased attitude regarding the use of alcoholic beverages by the adult citizen.

Dr. Mildred A. Weiss, Director of Psychological Services, Cleveland, Ohio, Center on Alcoholism:

There is an Ohio law which requires education in the public schools about the "harmful effects of narcotics and the effects of alcohol." It is left up to the schools how and what they will teach. Many of the school systems have looked to the Cleveland Health Museum and to the Cleveland Center on Alcoholism for help in carrying out this program. A manual and slides have been produced by the cooperative efforts of the Museum and the Center [see Selected Reading List]. The Museum has also produced a group of panel exhibits. The Cleveland Board of Education has developed its own manual and program based in part on this material.

The subject matter of the slides and manual is divided into five areas which may be presented as a complete course or separated and combined with other subjects. These areas are: (1) Drinking—"a well-established social custom"—which deals with material usually covered in social studies courses, such as nationality, socioeconomic level, and religious differences in attitudes toward the social use of beverage alcohol. (2) What alcohol is and where it comes from—its chemical structure and relationship to other substances —which would usually go into a science course. (3) The physiology of alcohol. (4) The psychology of drinking—why people drink and the psychological effects of drinking. (5) Alcohol and social problems—alcoholism comes in here and of course other social problems related to the use of alcohol, such as alcohol and driving, and alcohol and crime. This section of the course traces briefly the history of attitudes toward drinking and abnormal drinking, and also deals with social responsibility—what can be done about these problems. Hopefully, our present-day students will be able to accomplish what our generation could not.

Reverend Yvelin Gardner, Deputy Executive Director, National Council on Alcoholism:

For centuries churches have been looked to for a solution to deviant drinking behavior; when alcoholics could not be redeemed by the church they were punished by society. Prior to the development of modern knowledge on alcoholism, many churches supported temperance and/or total abstinence. Now, with allowance being made for various denominational differences, the churches are keeping abreast of new findings in this field and are aligning themselves with the rest of the community and other agencies in dealing with alcoholism.

A major indication of this is the 1958 proclamation of the National Council of Churches, "The Churches and Alcohol." Supported by one hundred diversified church groups, this document points out that the churches should share a pastoral concern for alcoholics and their families, and that when drinking reaches the point of alcoholism, all resources of church and pastor should be joined to aid the victim, who cannot deal with the problem without help. The Episcopal Church similarly has set up its own Commission on Alcoholism—making a statement on the theology of alcohol. This points out that alcohol, as one of God's creations, has a purpose which is good, although its excessive use cannot be condoned. The alcoholic, however, is considered to be a person who has reached a state of compulsive or addictive use, who has lost the freedom of choice, and should, therefore, be treated as a sick person.

Young people, whether in our church schools or elsewhere, must be approached "where they are" (that is, from the attitudes and position of youth) and not on the basis of adult wishes, attitudes, and ideas. Church school education in this respect should thus parallel the approach used in the public or private schools to avoid confusion among young persons. Private schools which are church-connected should inform themselves on the stand on alcoholism taken by the denomination to which the school belongs. There should also be open-minded communication between the church schools and other schools so that all will be teaching the same facts. The parents and the home form the third side of this "triangle." Family attitudes play the strongest part in influencing adolescent and college-age attitudes. It is only through the coordinated efforts of the church, home, school, and the community that effective measures against alcoholism can be taken.

The student point of view was represented at the symposium by a panel of selected students. Some of the panel members' comments follow:

Joseph Stetz, senior, Horace Mann School, New York, N. Y.:

There is no instruction at Horace Mann on alcohol as such. A little bit appears in general biology and science. I don't drink, although my family does—normally and socially. Regarding alcoholism and drunkenness, most of my fellow students consider it more or less something to laugh at. It may be a disease, but most of the fellows consider it to be mostly weak will.

Pamela Cantor, junior, North Shore Public High School, Great Neck, N. Y.:

We have a teacher who pre-tests us with a written paper which is not collected but is only for our own use on ideas about alcohol and alcoholism. As we go along, we find many of our original ideas were wrong. We don't use a text, but we see filmstrips dealing with alcohol in the bloodstream, different attitudes and misconceptions of students and different religious groups, some showing the development from normal drinking to the disease of alcoholism. A paper called "Alcohol and Adolescents" was taken home by us to our parents. We also had a term paper—a list of subjects on alcohol was given to us and we selected one in which we were interested. I think later on this knowledge will be of help to us. We won't laugh at it the way Joe's friends do. We know that it is a disease—that putting a man in jail is no cure because it does not reach the cause or change his attitude. I have noticed a big change even in one of the boys in my class who is usually a scoffer at all the teachers and drinks himself. He has listened, and we have talked about this freely, and there is a big change noticeable in him.

Robert Meringolo, junior, Polytechnic Preparatory Country Day School, Brooklyn, N. Y.:

We spend a few days on alcohol in physiology in the eighth grade and during one week in biology in our sophomore year. I think the boys would appreciate a program (not a course) where we could go into it a little deeper and see the social problems. So far, we have just discussed biological problems. I think a text booklet could be used so the teacher could refer to it. The program should be supplemented by films, about once a week. Giving us facts would also tend to help the students' emotional problems coming out of the home relating to alcohol.

Elizabeth Thornton, senior, Barnard College (graduate of North-field School for Girls, East Northfield, Mass.):

We did not have instruction on alcohol at the private school I attended. I think private-school people do have a problem on the subject of alcohol when they get to college—greater than that the public-school people have. I think that the program that Pam described was excellent. I feel that the age of sixteen or seventeen—just before a student leaves for college—is an effective age to wage a campaign of this sort. When you get to be a freshman, you can't look at it objectively—there are too many pressures.

An Educational Symposium for Practical Nurses

Practical nurses who attend alcoholic patients are in a highly strategic position for contributing to the arrestment of the disease, provided they have sufficient knowledge and understanding. Nurses, more than any other professional group, have direct contact with alcoholics and their families. If a nurse is informed about the basic elements of the disease and its symptoms, she can recognize early cases. By demonstrating understanding and warmth she can help motivate the patient to seek help and work toward his own recovery.

To increase nurses' knowledge of their role in treating alcoholics, a symposium was held in December 1966 in New York City, at which more than a thousand licensed practical nurses were present. Authorities in the field discussed the causes of alcoholism, the behavior of alcoholics, their care, and psychiatric approaches to treatment. Summaries of the speakers' remarks follow:

Dr. Vernelle Fox, medical director of the Alcoholism Rehabilitation Clinic, Atlanta, Georgia:

An underlying cause of the whole problem is being a human being in a stressful culture. The alcoholic who feels he is nine feet tall when drinking finds it more pleasant to live in a fantasy life. It is a kind of suicide with a loophole. Alcoholism reflects a deep-set problem, and drinking is the solution to the problem—as the alcoholic sees it. We must show the alcoholic a new solution; or else it is like telling a tuberculosis patient to stop coughing.

The alcoholic lacks a true commitment to life. He must resolve the struggle by becoming committed either to life or to death. The licensed practical nurse represents a real social force in this fight in that she can aid the patient to accept the fact that he needs help.

Theresa DiSalvatore, R. N., Westinghouse Electric Company, Springfield Gardens, New York:

Among the hundreds of thousands of recovered alcoholics in this country who are living serene and useful lives today, many not only thank God, but they also thank the nurse who said the right word or did the right thing when they were most in need of enlightenment, warmth and understanding. The nurse has the greatest opportunity to help the alcoholic and his family simply because she is in contact with him at the most crucial point on his road to recovery.

LPNs dealing with alcoholics need clinical knowledge of the early symptoms, especially at the time when the patient is not recognized as an alcoholic—possibly not even by his own doctor. When an alcoholic is admitted to a hospital, the LPN must understand that he needs the kind of close observation she would give a patient in shock or coma. The alcoholic is a very sick man, and he needs watching, especially if he is very agitated and unable to sleep.

In carrying out the doctor's orders, the nurse can do much to gain cooperation from the patient, as he awakens from his stupor and becomes aware of his situation. In respect to his physical care, emphasis should be placed on vitamin therapy, supplementing good nutrition and sometimes forcing fluids.

The nurse may be able to explain to the patient that alcoholism is a disease and that his body no longer can tolerate this chemical. This may be a new idea to him and one which can bring hope. The nurse has the greatest chance of being the alchoholic's "motivator" and can start him back on the road to good health.

Dr. Adele Streeseman, co-founder of the Brooklyn Y.W.C.A. School of Practical Nursing and former president of the New York Medical Society on Alcoholism:

The primary thing the alcoholic needs from the nurse is for her to raise his low self-esteem. The alcoholic feels that not only is the whole world against him, but he is against himself. Experience in treating alcoholics has revealed repeatedly that they are lacking in that "sense of preciousness that is every child's birthright." An alcoholic will transfer to the nurse the belief that she has the omnipotence and strength which he did not find in his parents. Through her ministrations, he will begin to establish some faith, trust and communication with another human being. Her friendliness will break down his vast sense of isolation.

The nurse must have a sense of kinship with the alcoholic and get across to him her belief that he is a reasonable and rational person. She must convince him she is on his side. It is she who is responsible for giving the outer support that must bolster his flagging inner resolve.

The nurse must let the alcoholic know that there is a long uphill road ahead and not allow him to become discouraged. She must convince him that she will never give up and that the war is not lost because of one battle. To help the alcoholic with his growth, tactful handling is essential.

The LPN in the Public Health field is in the unique position of meeting and helping the hidden alcoholic. She can be the best source of referral.

*Dr. Stanley E. Gitlow, associate clinical professor of medicine,
New York Medical College:*

This showing of LPNs [at the symposium] indicates that,
contrary to what the alcoholic believes, someone *does* care.
The nurse is in constant contact with the alcoholic and the
therapy is up to her. The doctor only sees the patient a small
part of a whole day's time, and the patient is suffering twenty-
four hours a day.

The alcoholic feels as if he were "skewered on a pitch-
fork" and the nurse must "smother him with that good old
tender, loving care." She can hold his hand and help him, and
she must get across to him that "treatment does work."

The Hospital Situation

One of the most shocking effects of the stigma formerly
attached to alcoholism is the refusal of many general hospitals
even today to accept alcoholic patients. A by-product of this refusal is the fact that many patients suffering primarily from alcoholism are admitted under other diagnoses. This subterfuge may
lead to improper treatment if nurses and attendants are not aware
of the patient's real condition. It has also resulted in a serious
falsification of statistics; many deaths primarily due to alcoholism
are camouflaged as resulting from other diseases.

In 1956 the House of Delegates of the American Medical
Association adopted a statement on the hospitalization of patients
with the diagnosis of alcoholism, which read, in part:

> Acute alcoholic intoxication can be and often is a medi-
> cal emergency. As with any other acute case, the merits of
> each individual case should be considered at the time of the
> emergency.
>
> The type of alcoholic patient admitted to a general hos-
> pital should be judged on his individual merits, consideration
> being given to the attending physician's opinion, cooperation

of the patient, and his behavior at the time of admission.

In order to offer house officers well-rounded training in the general hospital, there should be adequate facilities available as part of a hospital program for care of alcoholics. Since the house officer in a hospital will eventually come in contact with this type of patient in practice, his training in treating this illness should come while he is a resident officer. Hospital staffs should be urged to accept these patients for treatment and cooperate in this program. . . .

In order to accomplish any degree of success with the problem of alcoholism, it is necessary that educational programs be enlarged, methods of case findings and follow-up be ascertained, research be encouraged, and general education toward acceptance of these sick people be emphasized. The hospital and its administration occupy a unique position in the community which allow them great opportunities to contribute to the accomplishment of this purpose. It is urged that general hospitals and their administrators and staffs give thought to meeting this responsibility.[3]

The responsibility of the hospitals was equally recognized in a recommendation by the American Hospital Association in 1957, which stated, in part:

There are still many hospitals that deny admission to all alcoholic patients despite the availability of improved methods of treatment and demonstration by experience that only a minority of patients with acute alcoholism are uncooperative.

Such a policy denies to the alcoholic patient benefits which would be available to him were his acute poisoning from another source, such as food, etc. It also denies to hospital attending and house staffs opportunities for education in the management of the alcoholic patient.

The American Hospital Association urges general hospitals to develop a program for the care of alcoholics and, having done so, to base the decisions as to admission or non-admission of the patient with a diagnosis of alcoholism upon the condition and needs of the individual patient.[4]

In spite of the recommendations of these professional organizations, progress in respect to the admission of alcoholics for hospital care has continued to be slow. While improvements have been made, they have not been sufficient to meet the need. In 1966 the AMA found it necessary to reaffirm its 1956 statement and to adopt further recommendations on the subject. The remainder of this section is condensed from the AMA's 1966 report.[5]

In a survey jointly conducted by the American Hospital Association and the National Institute of Mental Health in 1964, 62 percent of the 5,200 hospitals returning questionnaires did not admit patients suffering from acute or chronic alcoholism. Among hospitals which routinely admit psychiatric patients for treatment somewhat over 60 percent admit and treat alcoholic patients. Of the hospitals which do not admit or treat psychiatric patients under any circumstances only 11 percent will admit acute alcoholics and only 6 percent will admit chronic alcoholics. Some of the hospitals which refuse to admit patients with the diagnosis of alcoholism have by-laws and charters which prohibit the admission of alcoholics. These have their roots in cultural attitudes which type the compulsive drinker as a moral renegade who is willfully misbehaving in drinking alcohol excessively. Reluctance to admit the alcoholic is rooted in beliefs that alcoholics are problem patients, uncooperative and difficult to handle.

In isolated cases an alcoholic may pose problems of control. Yet the trouble that he may give at such times is no greater than that given by a surgical patient coming out of his anesthetic, according to Marvin Block, M. D., member of the Committee on Alcoholism and Addiction of the AMA

Council on Mental Health. Ruth Fox, M. D., Medical Director, National Council on Alcoholism, adds that alcoholics "are usually cooperative and grateful if treated with respect and kindness. They can be quickly and safely sedated, and recover quickly, usually being up and about by the second day." [6] Dr. Fox has also outlined the need for admitting alcoholics to hospitals:

"Hospitalization is indicated to interrupt uncontrollable drinking or to combat the effects of the withdrawal state, which may lead to serious complications such as convulsions or delirium tremens. The general hospital is the best place to treat the acute alcoholic episode for a number of reasons. If the patient is comatose, a differential diagnosis is imperative, for the coma may be from a skull fracture, a cerebral accident, diabetes, etc. An elevated temperature may initiate delirium tremens, but it may also be due to an intercurrent infection. These questions can only be resolved in a general hospital, which offers full emergency equipment, full laboratory services, and a full consulting staff.

"Psychologically, hospital treatment has a profound effect on the alcoholic. Whereas he has formerly been treated as deliberately perverse, he is now considered an ill person, entitled to the same skillful attention given any other ill persons. His acceptance on the medical service of a good hospital may be the first step in his own acceptance of his illness, in his concept of himself as an individual who is ill and in need of treatment, and may pave the way for his further rehabilitation." [7]

The subterfuge of admitting patients under a false or secondary diagnosis creates dangers:

". . . nursing personnel were not alerted to the primary problem or if they soon found out, often resented the obvious subterfuge. They were not trained to handle such a patient on a general ward. The patient himself would be involved in the subterfuge, and this would be unlikely to add to his self-esteem. This, plus the hostility of the nurses, might aggravate his behavior even more. Finally, the physician, because of his own involvement in the subterfuge, and with both himself and the patient aware of it, might find himself unable to treat the patient in the most appropriate manner." [8]

Where subterfuge has been practiced, physicians and nurses have themselves had unfortunate experiences because they were not prepared to treat the basic alcoholism. Such experiences can be responsible for a great deal of the resistance to the hospitalization of the alcoholic.

In hospitals which do not admit patients with the diagnosis of alcoholism surveys might reveal that, in fact, many patients with this disease are regularly admitted. A review should be made of the charts of all patients admitted with the diagnoses of gastritis, gastroenteritis, and cirrhosis. Nurses', physicians', and interns' notes should be scanned for indications that the patient was intoxicated upon admission. Because of the high incidence of alcoholics involved in highway accidents, special attention should be given to emergency trauma admissions.

At its 1966 meeting, the AMA adopted recommendations that the medical societies work with hospital medical staffs and hospital associations to implement the AMA's 1956 statement, and that this statement be resubmitted to the Joint Committee on Accreditation of Hospitals with a request for all possible assistance in its implementation. The Association further recommended:

That in those hospitals which do not admit patients with the diagnosis of alcoholism, the governing board, administration, and medical staff consider feasible means for providing for the admission of such patients, including, where necessary, the revision of the hospital's charter and bylaws;

That in such hospitals, hospital medical staffs be encouraged to review for the previous year those charts where alcoholism might have been an admitting factor. If, in fact, alcoholics are being admitted, the hospital medical staff and governing authorities should be encouraged to take a more realistic approach to the admission and handling of these patients;

That insurance companies and prepayment plans be encouraged to remove unrealistic limitations on the extent of coverage afforded for the treatment of alcoholism, recognizing that alcoholism is a chronic illness and that multiple hospital admissions under medical supervision may be essential to arresting the progress of the disease.

In 1967 the Committee on Alcoholism and Drug Abuse of the Medical Society of the State of New York drew up a list of criteria for the admission to hospitals of patients suffering from alcoholism. This was the first action of the kind by a state medical society and is expected to be widely influential. The New York Society believes that similar criteria will eventually be adopted in many other states. Its criteria are listed in *Guide Lines for Admission of Alcoholics to Hospitals,* a pamphlet issued by the Smithers Foundation (see Selected Reading List).

* 8

THE LAW AND THE ALCOHOLIC

Recent landmark court decisions have defined clearly the legal standing and rights of alcoholics. All who come directly in contact with alcoholics should be familiar with the substance of these decisions. In essence they instruct the lower courts to view an alcoholic not as a criminal but essentially as an individual who suffers from a specific and treatable public health problem. This means in practical effect that courts must first consider the illness of alcoholism and only secondarily any possible criminal involvement.

For over 120 years the Correctional Association of New York has pioneered and crusaded for continual improvement in the administration of justice. Its interest in the chronic police-court offender stems from its insistence that alcoholics should not be prosecuted and punished for displaying a symptom of the disease of alcoholism but should be treated by health and welfare authorities.

The Legal Situation in Jailing Alcoholics

In a recent address,[1] Donald H. Goff, General Secretary of the Correctional Association of New York, analyzed the significance of the recent decisions. Excerpts from his address follow:

> The ferment in the administration of justice in the United States which began after World War II has recently merged with a similar ferment in the field of alcoholism. The

foundation for this junction was laid when the American Medical Association defined alcoholism as a disease in 1956.

A few clear-thinking individuals—notably a young Washington attorney, Peter Barton Hutt—recognized a fundamental inconsistency between the disease concept of alcoholism and the criminal prosecution of ill persons who displayed a symptom of this disease—namely, public intoxication. They began to question the state's right to criminally prosecute such persons for being publicly intoxicated.

A climax was reached early in 1966, which will go down in the history of both the administration of criminal justice and the field of alcoholism as the year of two major court decisions relating to the criminal prosecution and imprisonment of alcoholics on charges of public intoxication.

The first decision emanated from the Fourth United States Circuit Court of Appeals involving a Joseph B. Driver.[2] Mr. Driver, a fifty-nine-year-old alcoholic, had been previously convicted more than two hundred times and imprisoned nearly two-thirds of his life for being publicly intoxicated. His last conviction resulted in a two-year imprisonment sentence which was appealed. The Fourth United States Circuit Court of Appeals on 22 January 1966, after hearing the arguments both pro and con, vacated the criminal sentence for public intoxication of Joseph B. Driver, ruling that such a criminal sentence was "cruel and unusual punishment" and was in violation of the United States Constitution.

A second such decision handed down 31 March 1966 by the United States Court of Appeals for the District of Columbia in the case of Dewitt Easter,[3] also an alcoholic, ruled on the question of *mens rae* or criminal intent of an alcoholic to become publicly intoxicated. That court, likewise, ruled in favor of the appellant.

The direction of the handling of chronic police court alcoholics has been set by the two United States District Courts of Appeal, which in their respective districts (involving five states and the District of Columbia) now prevent the criminal prosecution or jailing of chronic alcoholics for public drunkenness. . . .

The United States Supreme Court was petitioned to hear another similar case (Budd vs. the State of California). After several months of study, the Supreme Court refused to grant a hearing on this case. This refusal leads one to speculate that because the health agencies had not prepared themelves to cope with this large number of alcoholics who were being given short jail sentences, and because the individual states had not equipped themselves with civil commitment laws, as contrasted to the criminal prosecution of alcoholics, to deal with those few alcoholics who might need state intervention for their own protection and the protection of the community, time was needed to fill the void which would be created before the complete shift from penal handling to medical-social treatment of some 150,000 to 400,000 alcoholics in the United States could be completed.

It is interesting to note that when the Supreme Court refused to hear the case, a minority opinion was written—a most unusual occurrence on a writ of certiorari, which leads many to believe that when the United States Supreme Court does hear such a case, its decision will follow that of the two Federal Courts of Appeal in 1966.

[Since this address was presented, the Supreme Court, during its October 1967–June 1968 term, heard a case of this nature.[4] However, the 5–4 decision was against the appellant.]

Change has been swift and deliberate in the United States in dealing with the chronic police court offender. Only ten years after the AMA classified alcoholism as a disease, the two major court decisions decided that to exhibit a symptom of the disease, public intoxication, was not in itself volitional, criminal behavior to be prosecuted and punished in the name of the state. This is an unusually short period of time in a free society for one aspect of a culture—in this instance, a medical definition—to become integrated with another aspect of the culture—the criminal code.

Based on the foundation laid by the medical profession, the two court decisions have acted as guidelines to a number of states. The more subtle effects, the more indirect effects, cannot be measured at this time. . . .

The United States Public Health Service and the National Council on Alcoholism have estimated that at the present time there are between four and six million alcoholics in the United States, and that the visual alcoholics—those found on skid row—constitute only from between 3 and 8 percent of these. Despite this, this small but visual group makes up approximately 50 percent of the population of the short-term-sentence penal institutions in the United States —individuals who because of being publicly intoxicated are in conflict with the law and as a result generally receive thirty-, sixty-, or ninety-day penal sentences to a local jail. These are the individuals whom I have labeled as "serving life sentences on the installment plan." They serve their sentence and within a relatively short time after being released, because of their addiction to alcohol, are arrested again for being publicly intoxicated, receive an additional sentence and continue the treadmill on which they have been since the inception of their illness.

One intensive study in New York State revealed that over 70 percent of the individuals serving penal sentences in a local correctional institution were there because of problems with alcohol. One person in his middle forties had already spent twenty years of his life in various correctional institutions throughout the country.

In their efforts to control the behavior of individuals, historically the sovereign states through laws prescribed acceptable and unacceptable behavior. Any deviation places the individual in conflict with the law and libels him to prosecution and punishment, either through fine or the loss of liberty. The underlying philosophy of the criminal code is that through the use of penalties individuals will be deterred from acting in an undesirable way and those who do commit crimes will be punished in the name of the state, in order that the community be protected from undesirable behavior or behavior deviating from the accepted. Both intoxication and alcoholism are considered deviations with which the state attempts to cope. In an effort to control the deviation of intoxication, many countries have made drunkenness in public an offense which evokes penalties. It is not possible to determine the effectiveness of such public intoxication laws in controlling the drinking pattern of those not addicted to alcohol, as it is not possible to assess accurately the deterring factor of any law. One must assume that the mere presence of a statute which reflects the generally accepted mode of behavior when enforced does affect the behavior of healthy, normal people.

However, the handling of penal institution commitment of the very symptom that would lead one to suspect alcoholism—namely, repeated offenses of public intoxication—has not only been ineffective but created a wide cleavage between the knowledge of the medical and behavior sciences on one hand and the practices of the administration of justice on the other.

The dilemma of handling cases of alcoholism involving chronic public intoxication appears to have been deeply rooted in the underlying philosophy of justice which looked at chronic public intoxication as a phenomenon controllable by traditional means. The dilemma was fed by local attitudes about alcoholism which were reflected in the belief that the disease could be "punished away." The two court decisions are changing this.

One of the outgrowths of the court decisions and the growing awareness of the futility of attempting to punish away a disease can be found in a bill introduced into the House of Representatives on 27 February 1967 (H.R. 6143). This bill would provide a comprehensive program for the control of drunkenness and the prevention and treatment of alcoholism in the District of Columbia. The bill states:

"The Congress hereby finds that:

"A. Dealing with destitute public inebriates as criminals has proved expensive, burdensome, and futile. The attendant expenditure of law enforcement resources is clearly excessive. The criminal law is ineffective to deter intoxication and to deal with what is basically a major public health problem—chronic alcoholism. Criminal punishment of alcoholics has helped to perpetuate the chronic drunkenness offender problem.

"B. Removal of public intoxication from the criminal system and establishment of a modern public health program for chronic inebriates facilitate early detection and prevention of alcoholism and effective treatment and rehabilitation of alcoholics. Handling of chronic inebriates through public health procedures relieves police, courts, correctional institutions, and other law enforcement agencies of an onerous and inappropriate burden that undermines their ability to protect citizens, apprehend law violators, and maintain safe and orderly streets.

"The Congress declares that:

"A. To control public intoxication and chronic alcoholism requires a major commitment of effort and resources by both public and private segments of the community. An effective response to these problems must include a continuum of detoxification, in-patient and out-patient treatment programs, and supportive health, welfare, and rehabilitation services. The District of Columbia shall establish and maintain a comprehensive model alcoholism program to which other communities may turn for study, guidance, and advice.

"B. Conduct that threatens physical harm to any member of the public or to property cannot be tolerated. The police shall continue to be empowered to handle as criminal any conduct by inebriates that endangers the safety of other citizens or of property."

The bill includes a civil commitment procedure which states:

"A. A judge of the District of Columbia Court of General Sessions may, on petition of the Corporation Counsel on behalf of the Bureau of Alcoholism Control, filed and heard before the seventy-two-hour period of detention for detoxification expires, order a person to be temporarily committed to the Bureau for in-patient treatment and care for a period not to exceed thirty days from the date of admission to a detoxification center, if, sitting without a jury, he determines that a person (1) is a chronic alcoholic, and (2) as a result of chronic or acute intoxication is in immediate danger of substantial physical harm.

"B. The courts in the District of Columbia are authorized and directed to take judicial notice of the facts set out . . . and to exercise their judicial responsibilities in a manner consistent with them. The courts may, in their discretion, commit to the Bureau for treatment and care for up to a specified period of time a chronic alcoholic who:

(1) is charged with a crime and who, prior to trial, voluntarily requests such treatment in lieu of criminal prosecution; or

(2) is charged with a crime and is acquitted on the ground of chronic alcoholism; or

(3) is convicted of a violation of section 25-128 of the D.C. Code and is found to be a continuing danger to the safety of other persons:

(4) *Provided*, that no term of commitment shall be ordered for a period longer than the maximum sentence that could have been imposed for the crime for which he was charged."

The bill proceeds to provide for legal protection such as the use of a writ of habeas corpus to challenge civil commitment and to provide counsel if the respondent is unable to afford one. It further provides for the retention of civil rights and liberties, such as the right of an ill person to refuse treatment for an ailment that presents no danger to the safety of other persons, the right of a patient to maintain the confidentiality of health and medical records, and the right to vote.

A second example of change in the United States emanates from the State of North Dakota which in 1966 had enacted a civil commitment procedure allowing for the commitment to state hospitals of individuals with a chronic addiction to alcohol. In 1967 several bills were introduced into that Legislature, one of which created a State Commission for the prevention of alcoholism and treatment of alcoholics in the State Commission of Mental Health and Mental Retardation. This division would act as the supervisory agency over individuals who, after having been civilly committed to the state hospital because of chronic addiction to alcohol, were released. The period of supervision extended for one year. In addition, the county court, upon advice and recommendation of this division, was authorized to recommit any person so released for an additional period not to exceed ninety days.

In the State of New York, a group of some twenty experts in the field of alcoholism appointed by the Interdepartmental Health and Hospital Council of the State spent eight months developing a comprehensive program which included a system of civil commitments coupled with voluntary in and outpatient treatment programs.

Even without the benefit of the two court decisions, the New York State Legislature upon recommendation of the Temporary Commission on Revision of the Penal Law and Criminal Code in 1965 enacted a new penal law which downgraded the offense of public intoxication in fifty-seven counties of the State from a misdemeanor with a six-months maximum sentence to a violation with a fifteen-day maximum sentence. It appears that the Temporary Commission recognized "the exercise in futility" of attempting to punish away the illness of alcoholics with a six-months sentence to a county jail. At the same time, the Commission recognized that, for the non-alcoholic who became publicly intoxicated, a fifteen-day sentence was sufficient to correct the behavior.

Within the City of New York, where it was not illegal to be publicly intoxicated, the charge of disorderly conduct was used to "sweep the Bowery." Appearing without counsel and often in an intoxicated condition, almost 100 percent of the defendants so charged were sentenced to short stays in the Workhouse. The legal point of whether being publicly intoxicated constituted disorderly conduct was questioned, and as an experiment, counsel was assigned in some 1,400 cases. When properly represented by an attorney, out of the 1,400 cases, convictions were had in only 7—disorderly conduct simply could not be proven. As a result, in June of 1966, the Police Department issued an order to its officers not to arrest individuals on disorderly conduct charges unless there was *prima facie* evidence that the individual was disorderly. Being publicly intoxicated was not enough. The number of disorderly conduct arrests dropped markedly in the City, the number of skid-row alcoholics appearing in the courts fell to a trickle, and the population of the Workhouse was greatly reduced. . . .

It is only a matter of time before several hundred thousand individuals in the United States can no longer be committed to "winter over in jail" but will become the responsibility of the health and welfare agencies rather than the police, courts, and correction.

Police Handling of Intoxicated Persons

Many people, at one time or another, come in contact with someone who, judging from outward appearances, has been drinking heavily. These indications may vary from appearances of extreme intoxication to stupor. Normally the onlooker wishes to help in the emergency. Yet the best of intentions may be ill advised if the basic cause of the predicament is other than the ingestion of too much alcohol, even though the helpless person may have alcohol on his breath. On the other hand, proper handling of the afflicted person may determine whether he lives or dies.

Because police officers are frequently confronted with this situation, a handbook for their guidance in recognizing and helping the intoxicated person or alcoholic was prepared by the Correctional Association of New York and the International Association of Chiefs of Police, with the cooperation of the Christopher D. Smithers Foundation, and widely distributed in the United States and other countries. The advice given to police officers can be useful to anyone confronted with such a situation, although the ordinary citizen should probably try to notify the police or a doctor as soon as possible. The remainder of this chapter consists of selections from the handbook.[5] (For the complete text, see Selected Reading List.)

IS THIS PERSON INTOXICATED?

One of the biggest obstacles in handling a case of drunkenness is that it is often difficult to distinguish between effects produced by alcohol or drugs and those produced by injury or illness. For instance, a person may smell of alcohol, and he may stagger and seem drunk . . . or lie unconscious in an apparent drunken stupor. Yet he may have had only a drink or two, or none, and blood or chemical tests would show that he is sober. For this reason it is important for a police officer or interested citizen to know something of other conditions which may produce symptoms mimicking alcohol intoxication. The most common of these are:

Diabetes. A person who is staggering and apparently drunk could be a diabetic suffering from low blood sugar—a condition that occurs in diabetics who have taken too much insulin or failed to eat enough to keep their blood sugar level up. Alternatively, the apparently unconscious "drunk" could be a diabetic in coma as a result of not having enough insulin. He may have alcohol on his breath, but there may also be present a peculiar sweetish odor caused by a substance called acetone which has accumulated in his blood (see chart).

Diabetes-Intoxication Comparison Chart [6]

	INSULIN REACTION	DIABETIC COMA	INTOXICATION
Cause	Too much insulin and lack of food	Lack of insulin	Too much alcohol in blood
Start	Sudden	Gradual	Gradual
Skin	Pale and moist	Flushed and dry	Flushed
Behavior	Excited	Drowsy	Stupor
Breath	Normal	Fruity odor	Liquor
Breathing	Normal to rapid shallow	Deep and labored	Slow
Vomiting	Absent	Present	May or may not be
Tongue	Moist	Dry	Moist
Hunger	Present	Absent	Absent
Thirst	Absent	Present	Absent
Sugar in urine	Absent or slight	Large amounts	Absent

Epilepsy.   Epileptics may sometimes wander about for hours in a confused state; some may even become violent for brief periods.

Head injury.   A serious possibility is the case of an apparently uninjured, apparently alcohol-influenced, accident victim. Some slight bleeding under the covering of the brain may at first produce confused symptoms similar to intoxication, or unconsciousness. If bleeding continues a clot forms which may press on the brain. Without immediate treatment the victim will die.

High blood pressure.   The victim of this disease in an acute state may become temporarily irrational.

Mental conditions, brain tumors, brain abscesses, brain infections.   These may give rise to unpredictable behavior and peculiar spells.

Stroke or apoplexy.   Both conditions are due to disturbances of blood circulation in the brain, and either can cause dizziness, confusion, vomiting or unconsciousness.

Degenerative diseases. Various degenerative diseases of the brain and nervous system may cause a person to stagger, act silly, be forgetful, or wander aimlessly.

Uremia. A form of kidney failure which can cause vomiting, convulsions and coma.

Wernicke's syndrome. A complication which may occur in alcoholism in which the victim—even when not drinking—is confused, has faulty muscular co-ordination, or may have paralysis of eye muscles.

Carbon-monoxide poisoning. This can cause dizziness, nausea, weakness, inability to walk, unconsciousness and, eventually, death. After the symptoms are well developed, the victim is usually a peculiar cherry-red.

Narcotic intoxication. Heroin users may appear drunken, drowsy, or even in deep sleep, but, unless in actual coma from overdosage, are readily aroused to alertness by gentle prodding.

All these are conditions that must be considered when you see a person behaving oddly or lying unconscious in the street. Instead of assuming that the person is drunk, the police officer or bystander should think: "There is a sick man in an emergency state and I'll have to do something about it." This is the safest course to take. If it subsequently turns out that intoxication was the sole cause, appropriate action can then be taken.

Breath odor is of little assistance in determining whether or not a person is intoxicated; wines and beer may produce the most distinct odors. Vodka has little or no aroma, and pure alcohol is virtually odorless. In addition, odoriferous gums and tablets can mask the foulest breath, so that a seasoned officer is unable to detect the smells of drinking. Paradoxically, however, breath odor is one area in which an officer can give an expert opinion in court; for example, whether or not it was tainted and, if so, with what?

HANDLING THE ALCOHOLIC

In handling the "drunk" or alcoholic in his course of duty, a police officer encounters many different problems. Knowing how to handle these could, in some cases, mean the difference between life and death. The very first problem will be to determine the extent of drunkenness. The officer must decide whether the person is in such a state as to be capable of hurting himself or others. If he does seem potentially dangerous, then he must be taken into custody, or at least protected.

The sleepy, depressed type must be handled with special care. He may appear quite capable of sleeping off his current state of intoxication. But he may have downed a pint or more of whisky, or equally potent drink, just before he was found, in which case he will get more and more intoxicated in the following hour or two. If left alone in a cell and not watched, he could die from the absorption of extra alcohol during that time. So the second problem involves the ability to recognize the common danger signs and complications of severe intoxication. Some of these are:

Coma. Initially the victim is drowsy, very sad, and sick. He may be aggressive when disturbed. Later he may develop some definite physical signs, such as skin pallor. Looking at him, you will see his eyes crossed or pointing out. He may complain of ringing in his ears, numbness "all over," and seeing double. His pulse becomes rapid; the eye pupils—tiny in the first stage—now become very large. Later he goes into increasing stupor from which it is difficult to arouse him, and he may die of one of two things:

Shock—signs are paleness, sweating, clammy skin, fainting and weak pulse.

Total anesthesia of the brain—this could happen within two or three hours after first seeing a drunken person.

Convulsions. These are a possibly frightening, possibly dangerous, development of the hangover stage. The immediate dangers are that the victim may fall and hurt himself or that his airway may become blocked—so-called swallowing of the tongue. The general danger is that the convulsion may indicate a very serious medical condition. The best treatment is to lay the convulsive patient on his back if possible, loosen any tight clothing, and put something soft, such as a rolled-up shirt tail, in the corner of his mouth. This will prevent him from biting his tongue and will give him an airway. After first aid has been administered, a physician should be called, and the person should be watched until medical advice is obtained.

Alcoholic hallucinosis. This may last from minutes to days. The victim sees and hears things that are not really there. He is convinced that they are there, and they may be vivid and terrifying. Sometimes he may have delusions (feeling perhaps that someone is after his life). Apart from these abnormalities, however, he is rational, can talk, knows who you are and what time of day it is. He doesn't usually have a fast pulse, fever, or tremor and is not sweating, pale or flushed. In fact, he looks all right, but "sees things."

Delirium tremens. This is a serious possible complication of the hangover stage. The person suffering from delirium tremens is out of contact with his surroundings and does not know what is going on, though there may be clear periods. He may not know where he is, what time of day or what month it is, or even what nationality he is. He often has some fever, is flushed, has a rapid pulse, and intense tremor. In addition, he has the typical disturbing hallucinations and suffers from insomnia and great exhaustion. Usually the condition lasts from two to seven days. Fortunately it is rare, but it is very serious and requires urgent medical attention.

In any of the circumstances described, first aid should be administered if indicated, and the person then should be taken immediately to the nearest medical facility.

EFFECTS OF INTOXICATION

The following table shows the symptoms normally associated with drinking and the resultant blood-alcohol concentrations in a drinker of average weight (about 160 pounds). It must be stressed, however, that this table can only be used as a very rough guide. In actual fact, the symptoms of different amounts of alcohol vary enormously with the individual.

DRINK CONSUMED	BLOOD-ALCOHOL (PERCENT)	EFFECTS
2 ounces 90-proof whisky, or about 2 12-ounce bottles American beer	0.05	Dulls top layers of brain controlling moral and physical judgment. The drinker loses some inhibitions, feels less bound by minor conventions and courtesies. He feels "on top of the world," and relaxes.
4 ounces 90-proof whisky, or about 4 12-ounce bottles American beer	0.1	Further affects moral and physical control centers. Drinker becomes gayer, may take some personal and physical liberties.
6 ounces 90-proof whisky, or about 6 12-ounce bottles American beer	0.15	Drinker begins to stagger and sway and speech may become slurred. Reflexes are slower. He becomes careless, over-confident, acts on impulse. Depending on the individual, lax moral behavior and/or careless driving are results of this amount of intoxication.
8 ounces 90-proof whisky, or about 8 12-ounce bottles American beer	0.2	Function of lower motor and sensory areas of brain is now definitely impaired. At this stage, virtually all drinkers, no matter how "seasoned," begin to show evidence of slowed reflexes and poor judgment—both morally and physically. The drinker may begin to see double and feel sleepy.

12 ounces 90-proof whisky, or about 12 12-ounce bottles American beer	0.3	There is now a marked unsteadiness of gait. The drinker is obviously drunk, needs help to walk or undress, and tends to fall asleep.
14 ounces 90-proof whisky, or about 14 12-ounce bottles American beer	0.35	Affects lower, more primitive areas of brain. Senses are dulled. Drinker falls into stupor.
14 to 20 ounces 90-proof whisky, or about 14 to 20 12-ounce bottles American beer	0.5 to 0.6	Usually "dead drunk." All consciousness goes. Apart from functions of breathing and heartbeat, drinker is almost anaesthetized.
24 to 28 ounces 90-proof whisky, or about 24 to 28 12-ounce bottles American beer	0.5 to 0.6	Puts to sleep the lowest level of brain, including center controlling the heart and respiration. Finally the heart stops. However, for alcohol to cause death in this way, more than a quart of whisky (or its equivalent) must be drunk in a short time.

The actual concentration of alcohol in the blood at any given moment depends on a number of other factors besides the amount drunk. Among these are the following:

Absorption. Absorption of alcohol into the blood stream is slowest in the stomach, quickest in the intestines. Consequently, a stomach already full of food delays absorption and slows the process of intoxication. Wine and beer contain food elements which also tend to slow up absorption of their alcohol content.

Weight. The build and weight of a drinker naturally tends to influence the speed of intoxication. In identical circumstances, a big man weighing 200 pounds would have to take twice as much alcohol as a slightly built woman weighing 100 pounds for both to reach the same concentration of alcohol in the blood.

Tolerance. There is no proof of any great difference among normal drinkers in physical tolerance to alcohol, but some drinkers apparently acquire what has been called a "psychological tolerance," being able to take fairly large amounts of alcohol without exhibiting obvious signs of intoxicated behavior. However, when their blood-alcohol concentration reaches a level in excess of o.3 percent, their "tolerance" is indistinguishable from that of anyone else. Tolerance may be lowered by exhaustion, emotional stress, and other conditions.

Oxidation. Alcohol is absorbed and distributed throughout the fluids of the body. Part of it (about 10 percent) is eliminated in the urine; very tiny amounts also through the breath and perspiration. The rest must be burned (oxidized) in the body like fats, sugars, and other foods. Only the liver can burn alcohol, though, and it does this at a fixed rate of ½ to ¾ ounce of 100-proof liquor per hour in an average-weight man. Nothing, not even physical exercise or cold baths, can speed up this rate. The following chart indicates how long, in a man of average weight, it takes alcohol to leave the body and reduce the blood-alcohol to a safe level.

After this many 1½-ounce drinks of 90-proof whisky, vodka, brandy, gin, or other alcoholic beverage . . .   *it takes this many hours for the body to burn the alcohol completely*

	0	1	2	3	4	5	6	7	8

O
OO
OOO
OOOO
OOOOO

PHYSICAL EFFECTS OF ALCOHOL

Obesity. As a food, alcohol, like pure fat or starch, supplies only calories. One 8-ounce glass of beer or a 1-ounce drink of 84-proof whisky each contains about 70 calories. Thus heavy drinking means extra calories in the diet. This can make the drinker fat.

Malnutrition. Alcohol is not a complete food. It contains no essential vitamins, minerals, or amino acids. Yet, as happens in years of excessive drinking, it can reduce appetite and replace balanced eating. This can lead to malnutrition.

Liver. Prolonged drinking of alcohol causes the liver to become swollen and yellow with fat (fatty degeneration). This often develops into a serious condition known as cirrhosis of the liver.

Nervous system. After prolonged excessive alcohol intake, damage can occur in the form of neuropathy or delirium tremens. In early neuropathy there is usually some tingling, numbness, burning pains, and weakness of the extremities. Delirium tremens is marked by hallucinations, severe tremor, insomnia, and great exhaustion. In extreme cases of long-lasting alcoholism, there may be permanent brain damage and mental illness requiring confinement in a psychiatric hospital.

Addiction. Alcohol in large doses is a narcotic and some people can become dependent or addicted. This is typified by the alcoholic whose drinking is undeterred by warnings, fines, or jail sentences. Such people are in need of specialized medical treatment.

SUGGESTIONS FOR POLICE OFFICERS

The relationship between alcohol and crime is complex. It cannot be said flatly that alcohol is a *cause* of crime, because that statement is too general. That it is a contributing factor in many cases is undoubtedly true. Police know that domestic quarrels, street fighting, and traffic accidents often have drinking or drunken persons involved. Drunken persons themselves are in danger of being victimized. They may be robbed or struck down in traffic. "Drunk cases" unquestionably provide many problems for police.

1. Police officers should be fully aware of the potential physical and mental effect of varying amounts of alcohol in the

body, have some understanding of the different diseases or conditions which may mimic the usual symptoms of alcohol intoxication, and know how to recognize the danger signs of alcohol intoxication (coma) or the hangover stage.

2. The police officer should determine whether or not the person is in such a state as to be capable of hurting himself or others. If he does seem potentially dangerous, he must be taken into custody or protected.

3. If the drunken person has to be jailed, the officer should ensure that the prisoner is watched at frequent intervals, in case intoxication should increase to possibly dangerous levels.

4. In any kind of comatose condition, where the prisoner cannot be aroused, police should call a doctor or try to get the victim to a hospital. If the coma lasts longer than a few hours, there are probably more complications than just alcohol.

5. The police officer should be fully aware of the disease of alcoholism and its possible complications.

A police officer is not expected to fulfill the function of the doctor, psychologist, or social worker. But to carry out his duties, he should make every effort to distinguish between the alcoholic and the person who has merely had too much to drink on a particular occasion. By knowing how to recognize and handle each properly, he can do much to help these persons, or, at the very least, do nothing to worsen the situation or contribute to death.

Remember, the alcoholic has a reputation for being uncooperative and requires a special kind of approach, one which demands a great deal of patience and fortitude on the part of the police officer.

Afterword

WHAT IS AHEAD?

Perhaps because so little had been done in a realistic manner before the 1930s in confronting the major public health problem of alcoholism in this country, the material which has been presented in the present book represents remarkable progress over the past thirty years.

The modern approach has produced significant advances over a wide spectrum of activity in establishing alcoholism as a disease and on this basis seeking to contain many of the tragic and inevitable results, if the disease is not checked by proper treatment. But we cannot become smug or complacent over this progress. As Dr. Jellinek pointed out (see Chapter 1), during the latter half of the nineteenth century a similar movement representing over forty years of earnest labor based primarily on the disease concept disappeared in the collective blackout known as National Prohibition.

This time a more vital and far-reaching effort is being made. In the renewed approach different and stronger forces have provided the impetus toward the eventual curtailment of this widespread malady. Each decade thus far has produced its own memorable contributions to the strength of the modern movement. The founding of Alcoholics Anonymous in 1933 was followed in the 1940s by the inception of the Yale Center of Alcohol Studies, the formation of the only voluntary health agency in the field—The National Council on Alcoholism—and the creation by legislative action in Connecticut of the first tax-supported state program on alcoholism.

During the 1950s official recognition of alcoholism as a disease came from the American Medical Association. (The principal reason for the earlier movement's demise was the failure of the medical profession to respond.) The 1960s produced support from the law through decisions in the lower courts (see Chapter 8).

What is ahead in the last decades of the twentieth century?

Upon the strong base thus far created to attack this gigantic health problem, significant advances can now be made in the three major areas—education, treatment, and prevention. Basic research in an effort to discover the causes of alcoholism should become the province of the Federal and state governments which are at last starting to do their share in a team effort with the various state programs and the voluntary and professional organizations in the field. The national and state governments can also contribute toward facilities for treatment at the hospital level. The establishment of community resources for treatment all over the country can also help to alleviate the tremendous damage alcoholism has done in the past.

Education at the secondary school and college level must provide all young people with knowledge of the warning signs of alcoholism for protection of their own health in later life, and of treatment resources available in their own communities.

Of equal importance in the alcoholism education program for the years ahead is more intensive instruction about alcoholism in the medical schools, law schools, and graduate schools of public health, social service, nursing, and other areas of learning.

Measures which have proven successful in dealing with alcoholism in one sector of American life can now be applied to other areas. "Constructive coercion" by industrial management and labor unions has proved remarkably effective in the rehabilitation of alcoholic workers through company programs. The motivation toward seeking treatment is prompted by the employee's concern for job security. This basic principle can be introduced into the area of drunken driving. The judge could suspend the alcoholic's driver's license for a year, or whatever period deemed necessary, during which the guilty person would be directed to seek treatment and eventually prove permanent rehabilitation from alcoholism before the license could be reinstated.

Alcoholism can eventually be restricted and controlled as a disease, just as tuberculosis and poliomyelitis have been brought under control during this century. But solution in this case can only result from unremitting and persistent effort on the part of the general public, the professional disciplines, and government agencies.

The American approach to alcoholism is by no means unique, as those who have attended international meetings on this problem can testify. Advancements abroad in education, treatment, and research are in some instances ahead of American ideas and execution. Through working together in attacking this major health problem, a common bond may be created among the peoples of the world, and a mutual respect developed which might produce important contributions toward world peace.

Appendixes

Appendix A

PROGRESSION OF ALCOHOLISM AND STEPS TOWARD RECOVERY

(Chart by Dr. M. M. Glatt, St. Bernard's Hospital, London; reprinted from The British Journal of Addiction, vol. 52, no. 2)

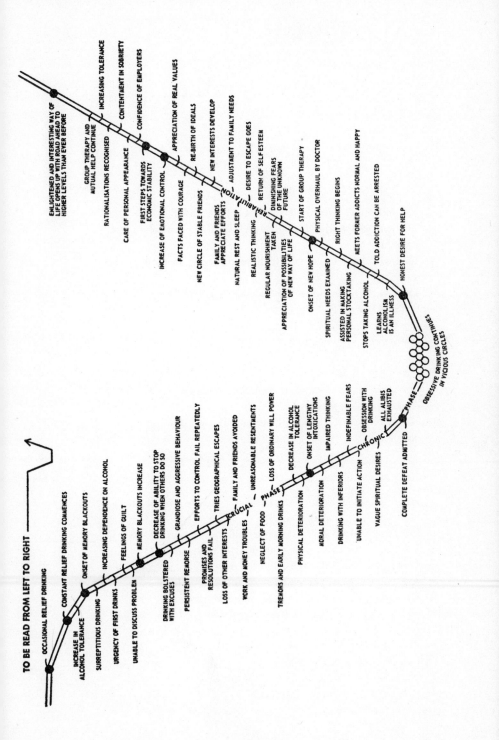

TO BE READ FROM LEFT TO RIGHT

OCCASIONAL RELIEF DRINKING

CONSTANT RELIEF DRINKING COMMENCES

INCREASE IN ALCOHOL TOLERANCE

ONSET OF MEMORY BLACKOUTS

SURREPTITIOUS DRINKING

INCREASING DEPENDENCE ON ALCOHOL

URGENCY OF FIRST DRINKS

FEELINGS OF GUILT

UNABLE TO DISCUSS PROBLEM

MEMORY BLACKOUTS INCREASE

DRINKING BOLSTERED WITH EXCUSES

GRANDIOSE AND AGGRESSIVE BEHAVIOUR

PERSISTENT REMORSE

DECREASE OF ABILITY TO STOP DRINKING WHEN OTHERS DO SO

PROMISES AND RESOLUTIONS FAIL

EFFORTS TO CONTROL FAIL REPEATEDLY

LOSS OF OTHER INTERESTS

TRIES GEOGRAPHICAL ESCAPES

FAMILY AND FRIENDS AVOIDED

WORK AND MONEY TROUBLES

UNREASONABLE RESENTMENTS

CRUCIAL — PHASE

NEGLECT OF FOOD

LOSS OF ORDINARY WILL POWER

TREMORS AND EARLY MORNING DRINKS

DECREASE IN ALCOHOL TOLERANCE

PHYSICAL DETERIORATION

ONSET OF LENGTHY INTOXICATIONS

MORAL DETERIORATION

IMPAIRED THINKING

DRINKING WITH INFERIORS

INDEFINABLE FEARS

UNABLE TO INITIATE ACTION

OBSESSION WITH DRINKING

CHRONIC — PHASE

VAGUE SPIRITUAL DESIRES

ALL ALIBIS EXHAUSTED

COMPLETE DEFEAT ADMITTED

OBSESSIVE DRINKING CONTINUES IN VICIOUS CIRCLES

LEARNS ALCOHOLISM IS AN ILLNESS

HONEST DESIRE FOR HELP

TOLD ADDICTION CAN BE ARRESTED

STOPS TAKING ALCOHOL

MEETS FORMER ADDICTS NORMAL AND HAPPY

ASSISTED IN MAKING PERSONAL STOCKTAKING

RIGHT THINKING BEGINS

SPIRITUAL NEEDS EXAMINED

PHYSICAL OVERHAUL BY DOCTOR

ONSET OF NEW HOPE

START OF GROUP THERAPY

APPRECIATION OF POSSIBILITIES OF NEW WAY OF LIFE

DIMINISHING FEARS OF THE UNKNOWN FUTURE

REGULAR NOURISHMENT TAKEN

RETURN OF SELF ESTEEM

REALISTIC THINKING

DESIRE TO ESCAPE GOES

NATURAL REST AND SLEEP

REHABILITATION

ADJUSTMENT TO FAMILY NEEDS

FAMILY AND FRIENDS APPRECIATE EFFORTS

NEW INTERESTS DEVELOP

NEW CIRCLE OF STABLE FRIENDS

RE-BIRTH OF IDEALS

FACTS FACED WITH COURAGE

INCREASE OF EMOTIONAL CONTROL

APPRECIATION OF REAL VALUES

FIRST STEPS TOWARDS ECONOMIC STABILITY

CARE OF PERSONAL APPEARANCE

RATIONALISATIONS RECOGNISED

CONFIDENCE OF EMPLOYERS

GROUP THERAPY AND MUTUAL HELP CONTINUE

CONTENTMENT IN SOBRIETY

INCREASING TOLERANCE

ENLIGHTENED AND INTERESTING WAY OF LIFE OPENS UP WITH ROAD AHEAD TO HIGHER LEVELS THAN EVER BEFORE

Appendix B

ARE YOU AN ALCOHOLIC?

To test yourself, answer the following questions as honestly as you can.

PHYSICAL SYMPTOMS	Yes	No
	3	7
1. Do you crave a drink at a definite time daily?		X
2. Do you feel under tension much of the time while not drinking?	X
3. Does drinking cause you to have difficulty in eating? Or sleeping?		X
4. Do you, at times, have the "shakes," extreme nervousness, or "dry heaves"?		X
5. Do you need a drink the next morning?		X
6. Have you been unable to get to work?	X
7. Do you lose time from work due to drinking?	X
8. Has your physician ever treated you because of drinking?		X
9. Have you ever been to a hospital or sanitarium because of drinking?		X
10. Have you ever had alcoholic convulsions? Delirium tremens?		X

MENTAL SYMPTOMS	Yes	No
	4	6
1. Have you ever had a "blackout" (complete loss of memory) as a result of drinking?	X
2. Do you drink to build up your self-confidence?	X
3. Do you drink to escape from worries or troubles?	X
4. Have you ever felt remorse after drinking?	X	X
5. Are you at times possessed with unreasonable fears?		X
6. Do you have feelings of guilt or inferiority?		X
7. Are you extremely sensitive to other people's opinions, particularly as they may relate to your personal life?		X
8. Do you drink because you are shy with other people?		X
9. Do you at times have feelings that people are watching you, following you, or talking about you?		X
10. Would you rather drink alone?		X

212

6 4

BEHAVIORAL SYMPTOMS   *Yes*   *No*

1. Have you become noticeably short-tempered, irritable, opinionated?   ___   X

2. Is drinking making your home life unhappy?   X   ___

3. Does your drinking make you careless of your family's welfare?   X   ___

4. Are you inclined to evade responsibility?   X   ___

5. Has your ambition decreased since drinking?   X   ___

6. Has your efficiency decreased since drinking?   X   ___

7. Is drinking jeopardizing your job or business?   ___   X

8. Have you ever gotten into financial difficulties because of drinking?   ___   X

9. Do you turn to lower companions and an inferior environment when drinking?   X   ___

10. Is drinking affecting your reputation?   X   X

SPIRITUAL SYMPTOMS   *Yes*   *No*

1. Do you lie about your drinking?   ___   X

2. Are you lying increasingly as a matter of course?   ___   X

3. Have you lost interest, affection, or love for other people?   ___   X

4. Have you become extremely self-centered and selfish?   ___   X

5. Do you blame others for the unhappy situation in which you find yourself?   ___   X

6. Do you hold bitter resentment toward certain people— wife, husband, employer, associate or friend—and do you continue to harbor these resentments?   ___   X

7. Are you still convinced that you can "run your own ship" in life, without outside help and advice?   X   ___

8. Have you lost faith?   X   X

9. Are you dishonest with yourself?   ___   X

10. Have you lost all self-respect?   ___   X

If you have answered YES to a majority of the questions in any section, you ARE an alcoholic.

Appendix C

DRINKING PHASES

(Adapted from *Business Week*, March 13, 1959)

	BEHAVIOR PATTERNS	AND WHAT EMPLOYERS SHOULD DO ABOUT THEM
NORMAL DRINKERS	The bulk of social drinkers, 80 million people, are here: anyone who takes more than five or six drinks a year but not enough to have formed a habit to the point of dependence.	No problem. These people generally can handle their liquor. It rarely interferes with their work.
EARLY SYMPTOMS	These people are considered "normal" drinkers even by their families. However, if they are properly educated as to early symptoms, they will know their drinking is not normal and that alcohol should not be used as a crutch. No party or other fun is complete without a "couple of drinks." They also drink for confidence. Continued "experiments" with liquor, if the drinker wonders if he is developing a problem, will soon show whether the pattern is veering toward later symptoms.	Very few of these drinkers come to the attention of employers. If they do, they should be told to watch their drinking carefully.
PROBLEM DRINKERS	These drinkers have discovered and are making full use of the pampering effects of alcohol. Here are the symptoms in the order they generally appear: (1) Abnormal drinking behavior, not always in quantity, but in attitude. They go beyond their group. (2) Blackouts—loss of memory of the night before.	Here's the toughest problem, yet the chief success of a company program on alcoholism can depend upon the alertness of supervision in spotting these employees. Not many people outside of family, friends, and close associates know how heavily these people drink. They are not alcoholics, but many of them will be

(4) Severe and chronic hangovers.

Employers, through early detection, can save most of these employees for many years of useful employment.

EARLY-STAGE ALCOHOLICS

These heavy drinkers, several million of them, have crossed the line to alcoholism. In virtually all cases, the only hope is abstinence. The progressive symptoms get worse:

(1) Loss of control. They say they "can take it or leave it alone," but they can't.

(2) Alibi system. There are many excuses available. Example: "I'm expected to drink in my business."

(3) Eye-openers. The old hair-of-the-dog for hangover cures.

(4) Changing the pattern, trying the "beer route" or wine. But not for long.

(5) Antisocial behavior, solitary drinking.

(6) Loss of friends, jobs.

(7) Medical aid sought.

Many companies are having success in rehabilitating drinkers in this stage. Company experts and outside clinics are used. But there are still difficulties: supervisors cover up; management is afraid to touch the situation; the drinker himself won't play ball. An efficient company program alleviates these difficulties.

CHRONIC ALCOHOLICS

Progress through the stages becomes more rapid. Symptoms become more glaring:

(1) Benders—several-day drunks.

(2) Tremors.

(3) Protecting supply—the bottle-hiding stage.

(4) Unreasonable resentments.

(5) Nameless fears and anxieties.

(6) Collapse of alibi system.

(7) Tinges of manic-depression. Almost completely anti-social.

You won't find many of these in the work force. They have by and large become unemployable. However, if their brain tissue has not been injured, they can be rehabilitated and many have been.

Appendix D

WHERE TO SEEK HELP

Alcoholics Anonymous. For alcoholics and their families. See local telephone book or contact *AA World Services, Inc.,* Box 459, Grand Central Station, New York, N. Y. 10007.

Al-Anon Family Group Headquarters, P. O. Box 182, Madison Square Station, New York, N. Y. 10010. For relatives and associates of the alcoholic.

Alateen, P.O. Box 182, Madison Square Garden Station, New York, N.Y. 10010. For teen-agers with an alcoholic relative.

National Council on Alcoholism. See local telephone book for the *Council on Alcoholism* nearest you, or contact the headquarters of NCA, 2 East 103rd Street, New York, N. Y. 10029.

COMMUNITY FACILITIES

Several major cities in the United States now maintain information and referral centers on alcoholism which can be contacted through the city's Health Department. Metropolitan New York has such centers in all five boroughs, maintained through the *Community Council of Greater New York,* 225 Park Avenue South, New York, N. Y. 10003.

STATE OR PROVINCIAL FACILITIES

To find the tax-supported state or provincial facility nearest you, write *North American Association of Alcoholism Programs,* Suite 615, 1130 17th Street, N. W., Washington, D. C. 20036.

FACILITIES IN FOREIGN COUNTRIES

Americans working abroad or stationed abroad with the armed services can find the nearest facility by writing the Executive Secretary, *International Council on Alcohol and Alcoholism*, Case Postale 140, 1001, Lausanne, Switzerland.

Information on the nutritional approach to the treatment of alcoholism can be obtained by writing *Dr. Roger J. Williams, Clayton Foundation Biochemical Institute*, University of Texas, Austin, Texas.

Reference Notes

Reference Notes

1. THE ALCOHOLISM COMPLEX

1. Lyndon B. Johnson, "Message from the President of the United States Transmitting Review of Achievements in the Fields of Health and Education and Further Recommendations for Attaining Goals" (89th Congress, 2nd Session, Document 395), 7.
2. The Cooperative Commission on the Study of Alcoholism, *Alcohol Problems: A Report to the Nation*, prepared by Thomas F. A. Plaut (New York: Oxford University Press, 1967).
3. J. W. Riley, Jr., "The Social Importance of Problem Drinking," *Social Forces*, 27 (1949), 301–305.
4. E. M. Jellinek, *The Disease Concept of Alcoholism* (New Brunswick, N. J.: Hillhouse Press, 1960).
5. Selden D. Bacon, "Alcoholics Do Not Drink," *Annals of the American Academy of Political and Social Science*, 315 (January 1958) 55–64.
6. John Ford, *Depth Psychology, Morality and Alcoholism*, (Weston, Mass.: Weston College Press, 1951).
7. World Health Organization, *Alcohol and Alcoholism—Report of an Expert Committee* (Technical Report 94, Geneva, 1955).
8. E. R. Goodenough, *Jewish Symbols in the Greco-Roman Period* (New York: Pantheon, 1956).
9. E. H. L. Corwin and E. V. Cunningham, "Institutional Facilities for the Treatment of Alcoholism," *Quarterly Journal of Studies on Alcohol*, 5 (1944), 10–85.
10. S. M. Bluestone, "Institutional Facilities for the Treatment of Alcoholism," *Quarterly Journal of Studies on Alcohol*, 5 (1944), 5.
11. R. Wlassak, *Grundriss der Alkoholfrage* (Leipsig: Hirzel, 1929).

12. A. D. Ullman, "The Psychological Mechanism of Alcohol Addiction," *Quarterly Journal of Studies on Alcohol*, 13 (1952), 602–608.
13. E. E. Lape, E. M. Phillips, and M. T. Edgar, *Medical Research: A Mid-Century Survey* (Boston, Little, Brown & Co., 1955), vol. II, chapter 9.

3. THE PERILS OF CONTROLLED DRINKING

1. J. E. Shea, "Psychoanalytic Therapy and Alcoholism," *Quarterly Journal of Studies on Alcohol* 15 (1954), 595.
2. Marvin A. Block, *Alcoholism: Its Facets and Phases* (New York: The John Day Company, 1962), 23–24.
3. Bacon, *op. cit.*, 60–64.
4. D. L. Davies, "Normal Drinking in Recovered Alcohol Addicts," *Quarterly Journal of Studies on Alcohol*, 23 (1962).
5. E. M. Pattison, E. G. Headley, G. C. Gleser, and L. A. Gottschalk, "The Relation of Drinking Patterns to Overall Health in Successfully Treating Alcoholism" (mimeographed; University of Cincinnati College of Medicine, Departments of Psychiatry and Preventive Medicine, Cincinnati, Ohio, 1965).
6. Davies, *op. cit.*
7. Davies, "Response by Dr. Davies," *Quarterly Journal of Studies on Alcohol*, 24 (1963), 331.
8. Ruth Fox, "Comment on the Article by Dr. Davies," *Quarterly Journal of Studies on Alcohol*, 24 (1963), 117.
9. Marvin A. Block, *ibid.*, 114–117.
10. Harry N. Tiebout, *ibid.*, 109–111.
11. M. M. Glatt, *ibid.*, 26 (1965), 116–117.

4. SOME PHYSIOLOGICAL ASPECTS

1. *A Symposium on the Biochemical and Nutritional Aspects of Alcoholism* (New York: The Smithers Foundation, 1964). Other speakers were William Shive, Ph.D., Chairman, Department of Chemistry, and Clayton Foundation Biochemical Institute, University of Texas, Austin: Glutamine as a General Metabolic Agent Protecting Against Alcohol Poisoning; Frank L. Siegel, Ph.D., Joseph P. Kennedy, Jr., Laboratory, Department of Pediatrics, University of Wisconsin Medical School, Madison: Plasma Amino Acid Patterns in Alcoholism;

J. H. Quastel, Ph.D., D. Sc., Department of Biochemistry, McGill University, and Director, McGill-Montreal General Hospital Research Institute, Montreal, P. Q., Canada: Effects of Alcohols on Brain Metabolism; Bert L. Vallee, M.D., Department of Medicine, Harvard Medical School, Boston, Massachusetts; Enzymatic Aspects of Alcoholism; Jack H. Mendelson, M.D., Department of Psychiatry, Massachusetts General Hospital, Boston, discussant; Seymour Kety, M.D., Chief, Laboratory of Clinical Science, National Institute of Mental Health, Bethesda, Maryland, discussant.

2. Roger J. Williams, *Biochemical Individuality* (New York: John Wiley & Sons, 1956).

3. M. F. Trulson, R. Fleming, and F. J. Stare, "Effectiveness of Vitamin B Complex Administration in Alcoholism Control," *Journal of the American Medical Association*, 155 (1954), 114–119.

4. Roger J. Williams, *Alcoholism: The Nutritional Approach* (Austin: University of Texas Press, 1959).

5. A FAMILY ILLNESS

1. Marvin A. Block, "If There's an Alcoholic in the Family," *Parents' Magazine*, November 1964.

2. Harrison M. Trice, *Alcoholism in America* (New York: McGraw-Hill, 1960), 64–69.

3. Marvin A. Block, *Alcoholism: Its Facets and Phases, op. cit.,* 74.

6. A MAJOR HEALTH PROBLEM FOR INDUSTRY

1. Charles P. Frazier, "The Billion Dollar Hangover," New York *World-Telegram and Sun*, April 10, 1957, 22.

2. Kemper Insurance Company, *A Neglected Area of Loss Reduction: What to Do About the Employee with a Drinking Problem* (Chicago: Kemper Insurance Company, 1966).

3. Metropolitan Life Insurance Company, *Alcoholism* (New York: Metropolitan Life Insurance Company, 1967).

4. R. B. Smithers, "Alcoholism: An Economic Problem" (mimeographed; The Christopher D. Smithers Foundation, New York, 1964).

5. The National Industrial Conference Board, *The Alcoholic Worker* (New York: National Industrial Conference Board, 1958).

6. Harrison M. Trice, "New Light on Identifying the Alcoholic Employee," *Personnel* (published by the American Management Association), 41 (1964), 18–25.
7. Harrison M. Trice, *The Problem Drinker on the Job* (Ithaca, N.Y.: New York State School of Industrial and Labor Relations, Cornell University, 1958), 17–18.
8. Western Electric Company, *Policy and Program—Employees With Drinking Problems: A Guide for Supervisors* (New York: Western Electric Company, 1962).
9. Arnold J. Pfeffer, *Alcoholism* (New York: Grune & Stratton, Inc., 1958).
10. In *A Company Program on Alcoholism—Basic Outline* (New York: Christopher D. Smithers Foundation, 1959), 41.
11. Harrison M. Trice, *Alcoholism in Industry—Modern Procedures,* (New York: Christopher D. Smithers Foundation, 1961), 60.
12. Leo Perlis, "Alcoholism: A Challenge to Labor and Management" (mimeographed; National AFL-CIO Community Service Activities, Washington, D. C., 1964).

7. ALCOHOL EDUCATION: SOME SIGNIFICANT AREAS

1. The preceding paragraphs have been excerpted from "Effective Education on Alcoholism," an address by R. B. Smithers delivered at the 10th European Summer Institute for the Prevention and Treatment of Alcoholism, London, England, August 13, 1964.
2. *Alcohol Education in the Private Schools: A Symposium* (New York: The Christopher D. Smithers Foundation, 1960).
3. American Medical Association, *House of Delegates Proceedings,* November 1956, 32–33.
4. *Hospitals,* 31:106, December 1, 1957.
5. American Medical Association, *Proceedings, House of Delegates,* November–December 1966.
6. Ruth Fox, M. D., "The Alcoholic in the General Hospital," *Frontiers in General Hospital Psychiatry,* Louis Linn, M. D., ed. (New York: International Universities Press, Inc., 1961).
7. *Ibid.*

8. Mark Berke, Jack D. Gordon, Robert I. Levy, and Charles B. Perrow, *A Study of the Nonsegregated Hospitalization of Alcoholic Patients in a General Hospital.* Hospital Monograph Series, No. 7 (Chicago: American Hospital Association, 1959).

8. THE LAW AND THE ALCOHOLIC

1. Donald H. Goff, address delivered at the Thirteenth International Institute on the Prevention and Treatment of Alcoholics, Zagreb, Yugoslavia, June 1967.
2. U. S. Court of Appeals for the 4th Circuit, No. 1000166, Joseph B. Driver, Appellant, v. Arthur Hinnant, Superintendent, Halifax County Prison Unit of the North Carolina State Prison Department, Appellee, 22 January, 1966.
3. U.S. Court of Appeals, District of Columbia Circuit Court, No. 19365, Dewitt Easter, Appellant, v. District of Columbia, Appellee, 31 March, 1966.
4. Supreme Court of the United States, No. 405, Leroy Powell, Appellant, v. The State of Texas, Appellee, On Appeal from the County Court at law No. 1 of Travis County, Texas, October Term, 1967.
5. The Correctional Association of New York and The International Association of Chiefs of Police, *Alcohol and Alcoholism, A Police Handbook,* March 1965.
6. Information on diabetes obtained from the American Diabetes Association, 18 East 48th Street, New York, N. Y. 10017.

Selected Vocabulary

Selected Vocabulary

The following vocabulary is reprinted from *The Alcohol Language* by Mark Keller and John R. Seeley (Toronto, Canada: University of Toronto Press, 1958). Terms used in the text which are not given in this list are defined when they are first used.

NOTE: The inclusion of a definition here does not imply "correctness," but only that the term has been used as defined. Where several numbered definitions of a term are given, precedence usually indicates preferred usage. The selection of items was arbitrary. For the most part, they are those known to have given trouble in usage or to be allied to trouble-giving terms.

ABSTAINER. One who practices abstinence.

ABSTINENCE. Total abstinence; refraining completely from drinking any alcoholic beverage.

ACUTE ALCOHOL INTOXICATION. 1. Alcohol intoxication; severe alcohol intoxication; alcohol poisoning. 2. A circumscribed episode of alcohol intoxication as distinguished from a continual or prolonged state of intoxication.

ACUTE ALCOHOLIC STATE. 1. A physical or mental disorder of alcoholics, associated with and immediately consequent to a prolonged bout, as acute alcoholic hallucinosis, acute Korsakoff's psychosis, delirium tremens, postalcoholic psychomotor agitation. 2. Alcohol intoxication.

ACUTE ALCOHOLISM.[1] 1. Alcohol intoxication or alcohol poisoning. 2. A state of intoxication in an alcoholic. 3. The temporary disturbances or the acute alcoholic states due to excessive drinking.

ADDICTION. *See* ALCOHOL ADDICTION; DRUG ADDICTION.

[1] The unambiguous definition of ALCOHOLISM appears to render the term "acute alcoholism" ambiguous. *Cf.* ALCOHOLISM; ALCOHOL INTOXICATION.

ADDICTIVE DRINKER. A person who manifests the behavior or symptoms of alcohol addiction.

ADDICTIVE DRINKING. Alcohol addiction.

ALCOHOL. 1. Ethyl alcohol (ethanol, CH_3CH_2OH) when the type is not specified; a colorless, volatile, slightly aromatic, flammable liquid, one of the products of vinous fermentation. Distinguished from alcoholic beverages, of which it is the characteristic and essential ingredient, and from other alcohols, as isopropyl, methyl, etc. 2. Distilled alcoholic beverages as distinguished from wine, beer, etc.

ALCOHOL ADDICT. A person who manifests the behavior or symptoms of alcohol addiction.

ALCOHOL ADDICTION. 1. An overwhelming desire, need, impulse, or compulsion to drink and to obtain alcoholic beverages by any means, with psychological and possibly physiological dependence on alcohol, marked by a tendency to be unable to stop when drinking is begun. Distinguished from drug addictions in which there is, in addition, a tendency to increase the dose, and in which physiological dependence is much more probable. 2. Alcoholism.[2]

ALCOHOL CONCENTRATION. The proportion of alcohol in a tissue or fluid, expressed as volume or weight of alcohol per volume or weight of fluid or tissue.

ALCOHOL INTOXICATION. 1. A state of pronounced disturbance of function resulting from the presence of alcohol in the central nervous system. (Cf. UNDER THE INFLUENCE OF ALCOHOL.) 2. Drunkenness. 3. Alcoholism or inebriety.

ALCOHOL PATHOLOGY. 1. Any morbid change caused by the direct or indirect effects of alcohol. 2. Any individual or social harm resulting from inebriety.

ALCOHOL POISONING. A severe or extreme state of alcohol intoxication.[3]

ALCOHOL TOLERANCE.[4] 1. The capacity to maintain normal function in

---

[2] For distinction between ALCOHOLISM and ALCOHOL ADDICTION, see footnote 7.

[3] Alcohol poisoning appears to be distinguished from alcohol intoxication (definition 1) only by the severity of involvement. It would be advantageous to define the difference in terms of alcohol concentration in the blood, for example, "alcohol poisoning is an extreme state of intoxication, usually at alcohol concentrations in the blood above 0.4 per cent." The demarcation point of 0.4 per cent would allow parallel clinical discrimination by the symptom of loss of consciousness.

[4] This term has frequently been used ambiguously. To avoid misunderstanding, the idea of definition 3 might be expressed by another term, for example, alcohol adaptation. The use of ALCOHOL TOLERANCE as in definition 4 apparently stems from a popular misunderstanding of physiology and is without semantic merit.

the presence of a given concentration of alcohol in the tissues. 2.
The functional capacity of the organism after the intake of given
amounts of alcohol. 3. The adaptation of the organism to the continued, repeated, or increased presence of alcohol in the tissues.
4. The efficiency of the organism in handling or disposing of alcohol.

ALCOHOLIC (*noun*). 1. A person whose behavior or condition complies
with a definition of alcoholism. 2. A person who drinks alcoholic
beverages to excess.[5]

ALCOHOLIC BEVERAGE. Any beverage containing alcohol, as beer, cider,
distilled spirits, wine.

ALCOHOLIC DISEASE. Any physical or mental complication of alcoholism;
a disorder occurring relatively frequently in alcoholics and caused
by the direct or indirect effects of alcohol on the organism, as cirrhosis of the liver, delirium tremens, Korsakoff's psychosis, polyneuropathy.[6]

ALCOHOLIC PSYCHOSIS. Any mental disorder occurring relatively frequently in alcoholics and caused by the direct or indirect effects of
alcohol on the organism, as delirium tremens, Korsakoff's psychosis.

ALCOHOLISM. 1. A chronic disease, or disorder of behavior, characterized by the repeated drinking of alcoholic beverages to an extent
that exceeds customary dietary use or ordinary compliance with
the social drinking customs of the community, and that interferes
with the drinker's health, interpersonal relations, or economic functioning. 2. Excessive drinking of alcoholic beverages characterized
by the likelihood of loss of control over drinking when some alcoholic beverage is ingested or when an individual critical alcohol
level in the blood has been attained.[7] 3. Alcohol addiction.[7] 4. Al-

---

[5] Definition 2, of wide popular acceptance, equates alcoholic with excessive
drinker (*cf.* EXCESSIVE DRINKING) and thus blurs the useful and important distinction between the two terms.

[6] This definition excludes disorders to which excessive drinking may render the
individual more susceptible (as accidents) or less resistant (as infections).

[7] Discriminating usage would reserve the term ALCOHOLISM for the condition
described in definition 1; the condition described in definition 2, which involves
LOSS OF CONTROL, would be called ALCOHOL ADDICTION rather than alcoholism. Accordingly, definition 3, which equates alcoholism and alcohol addiction, would be
ambiguous. It must be observed, however, that the discrimination necessary for
distinguishing between alcoholism and alcohol addiction may require individual
diagnosis. The practical consequence of this appears to be that the term ALCOHOL-
ISM must be understood as probably including alcohol addiction except when the
two are expressly distinguished. Determining the meaning of ALCOHOLISM in the
literature at present may require close attention to context.

cohol poisoning or alcohol intoxication.[8] 5. A diseased condition caused by excessive drinking.[9] 6. (*popular*) Drunkenness; excessive drinking; inebriety.[10]

ALCOHOLISM WITH COMPLICATIONS. 1. Alcoholism marked by any defect of health consequent to excessive drinking. (*Cf.* CHRONIC ALCOHOLISM, definition 1.)

ALCOHOLIST.[11] 1. An alcoholic. 2. A person whose drinking constitutes an abuse of alcohol. 3. A user of alcoholic beverages, as distinguished from an alcoholic.

BENDER (*slang*). A spree, a bout.

BLACKOUT. 1. Amnesia for the events of any part of a drinking episode, without loss of consciousness.[12] 2. Coma or stupor due to alcohol intoxication.

CHRONIC ALCOHOL INTOXICATION. 1. A prolonged state of alcohol intoxication maintained by repeated intake of alcohol before or soon after previously taken alcohol has been metabolized. Distinguished from alcoholism or inebriety. 2. Alcoholism or inebriety.

CHRONIC ALCOHOLIC.[13] 1. A person who has chronic alcoholism. 2. An alcoholic.

[8] Definition 4 has only the slight virtue of allowing the briefer form, ALCOHOLISM, to be used in place of ALCOHOL POISONING (or ALCOHOL INTOXICATION); against this is the ambiguity arising from the fact that ALCOHOLISM is most often used to name the alcoholic's abnormality of behavior, as in definitions 1 and 2, rather than its consequences.

[9] Definition 5 appears to be inherently ambiguous. It is not clear whether the "diseased condition" is the alcoholism (which implies that excessive drinking causes or is caused by excessive drinking) or some other disorder due to inebriety, that is, a medical complication of alcoholism or chronic alcoholism (*cf.* CHRONIC ALCOHOLISM, definition 1).

[10] The use of ALCOHOLISM in place of DRUNKENNESS, EXCESSIVE DRINKING, or INEBRIETY, as in definition 6, appears to be a popular misappropriation of a technical word.

[11] This term is rare in the United States but common in the Scandinavian countries where it is used chiefly in the sense of definition 2. It is analogous also to the Italian *alcoolist* (ALCOHOLIC, definition 1).

[12] This usage is American and has the same meaning as the slang term "pulling a blank." Pulling a blank—that is, blanking out—may have originally taken the form "blankout," by analogy with the popular term "blackout" (which referred to *amaurosis fugax*), and from that became corrupted to BLACKOUT. Definition 2 is the British usage.

[13] When used to designate an alcoholic this term is redundant, since an alcoholic is by definition suffering from a chronic disorder. Because of worldwide ambiguous definitions and uses of this term, its abandonment has been recommended by the Subcommittee on Alcoholism of the World Health Organization. In the literature, the term should be interpreted in accordance with context.

CHRONIC ALCOHOLISM.[14] 1. Alcoholism with complications; physical or psychological changes due to the prolonged excessive use of alcohol. 2. Alcoholism, alcohol addiction, or repeated drunkenness. 3. Long-lasting inebriety or alcoholic disorder.

DEBAUCH. A spree, a bout.

DIPSOMANIA. 1. Periodic excessive drinking. (*Cf.* PERIODIC DRINKING.) 2. Craving, or periodic craving, for alcohol. 3. Alcoholism.

DISTILLED SPIRITS. 1. Alcoholic beverages produced by distillation and containing, usually, 25 percent or more alcohol, as brandy, cordials, gin, rum, whisky, etc. 2. Alcohol.

DRINKER. 1. One who partakes of alcoholic beverages to any extent. Distinguished from abstainer. 2. (*popular*) An alcoholic; an excessive drinker, a drunkard.[15]

DRINKING. Partaking of alcoholic beverages; not abstaining.

DRUG ADDICTION. An overwhelming desire, need, or compulsion to take a drug and to obtain it by any means, with a tendency to increase the dose and with psychological or physiological dependence on the drug. Distinguished from alcohol addiction, in which there is no tendency to increase the dose and physiological dependence is relatively questionable.

DRUNK (*noun; slang*). 1. One who is intoxicated or under the influence of alcohol. 2. An alcoholic. 3. An episode of drunkenness, a spree.

DRUNKENNESS. 1. Alcohol intoxication. 2. Inebriety.

DRY. 1. (*noun*) One who is opposed to drinking or to the promotion of the use of alcoholic beverages. 2. (*adjective, applied to an alcoholic*) Abstinent.

EXCESSIVE DRINKING. 1. The drinking of alcoholic beverages to an extent that exceeds customary dietary use or ordinary compliance with the social drinking customs of the community. 2. Inebriety.

HANGOVER. The immediate pathophysiological or pathopsychological after-effects of drinking, usually of large amounts, other than effects of the presence of alcohol.

---

[14] In the sense of definitions 2 and 3 this term is tautological or ambiguous. Because of worldwide ambiguous definitions and uses of this term, its abandonment has been recommended by the Subcommittee on Alcoholism of the World Health Organization. The term ALCOHOLISM WITH COMPLICATIONS may be substituted when the sense of definition 1 is intended. When occurring in the literature the meaning of CHRONIC ALCOHOLISM must be interpreted, when possible, according to context.

[15] The use of this term according to definition 2 is grossly ambiguous.

HIGH (*slang*). Under the influence of alcohol to a mild degree, less than TIGHT.

INEBRIATE (*noun*). 1. An excessive drinker. 2. An alcoholic.

INEBRIETY. 1. Excessive drinking. 2. Alcoholism.

INTEMPERANCE. 1. Immoderate drinking. 2. Drunkenness.

INTOXICATION. Alcohol intoxication when another cause is not specified.

LIQUOR. 1. Distilled spirits. 2. Any alcoholic beverage.

LOSS OF CONTROL OVER DRINKING. The inability, whether on some or on all occasions, to stop voluntarily when some alcoholic beverage is ingested. Said to be characteristic of alcohol addiction (*Cf.* ALCOHOL ADDICTION; ALCOHOLISM, definition 2) and distinguished from deterioration of motor coordination or of social propriety under the influence of alcohol.

MODERATE DRINKING. The drinking of alcoholic beverages in such amounts and frequencies as to comply with the dietary or customary usages of the community, without involvement in pathological behavior or consequences.

MODERATION. Moderate drinking.

NONADDICTIVE ALCOHOLIC. A nonaddictive pathological drinker.

NONADDICTIVE PATHOLOGICAL DRINKER. A person who drinks excessively as a means of handling unconscious problems, and with consequent pathologies, but who does not manifest the overwhelming desire, need, impulse or compulsion, or the loss of control, characteristic of alcohol addiction.

PATHOLOGICAL DRINKER. 1. A person whose drinking causes alcohol pathologies. 2. A person who drinks excessively as a means of handling unconscious problems; an alcoholic. 3. A problem drinker.

PATHOLOGICAL INTOXICATION. 1. An extraordinary reaction to small amounts of alcohol, marked by violent behavior followed by amnesia. 2. A reaction of senseless furor or violence after drinking, with amnesia for the episode.

PATHOLOGICAL REACTION TO ALCOHOL. Pathological intoxication.

PERIODIC DRINKING.[16] A form of alcoholism characterized by bouts of excessive drinking with sustained intervals of abstinence or moderate drinking.

POST-INTOXICATED STATE. 1. Immediate sequels of an alcoholic bout, in-

[16] A more correct but still not quite precise term for this condition would be periodic alcoholism.

cluding anxiety, psychomotor agitation, and other symptoms, sometimes attributed to alcohol withdrawal. 2. Delirium tremens, acute alcoholic hallucinosis, or other disorders, chiefly of the nervous system, which may become manifest in alcoholics after a prolonged bout. 3. Hangover.

PROBLEM DRINKER. 1. A person who drinks alcoholic beverages to an extent or in a way that causes private or public harm. 2. An excessive drinker.

SOBER. 1. Not under the influence of alcohol. 2. (*said of an alcoholic*) No longer drinking.

SOBERING UP. Detoxication after a spree.

SOBRIETY. 1. Temperance. 2. (*said of an alcoholic*) The ability to refrain from drinking.

SOCIAL DRINKING. 1. Moderate drinking on social occasions. 2. Drinking to comply with the expectation of companions. 3. Drinking in a way and within the limits accepted by a cultural group.

SPIRITS, SPIRIT. Distilled spirits.

SPREE. An episode of prolonged excessive drinking.

SPREE DRINKING. Periodic drinking.

SYMPTOMATIC ALCOHOLISM. Alcoholism secondary to a distinct clinical entity, as mental deficiency, psychoneurosis, or psychosis.

SYMPTOMATIC DRINKING. 1. Drinking, usually excessive, as a means of handling overt tensions and unconscious problems, or as a symptom of a mental disorder. 2. Drinking, usually excessive, for relief from pain; or alcoholism as a response to unbearable pain.

TEMPERANCE. 1. Moderation. 2. Abstinence.

TIGHT (*slang*). Under the influence of alcohol, more so than HIGH.

TOLERANCE. *See* ALCOHOL TOLERANCE.

UNDER THE INFLUENCE OF ALCOHOL.[17] A state of relatively mild disturbance of function resulting from the presence of alcohol in the central nervous system. (*Cf.* ALCOHOL INTOXICATION.)

USER. One who partakes of alcoholic beverages to any extent; a drinker. Distinguished from abstainer.

WET. 1. A person engaged in promoting the use of alcoholic beverages. 2. One who takes a stand favorable to alcoholic beverages, specif-

[17] UNDER THE INFLUENCE OF ALCOHOL is defined by law in some jurisdictions in terms of specified concentrations of alcohol in body tissues or fluids. It is sometimes distinguished from alcohol intoxication (or drunkenness), for which higher alcohol concentrations are specified.

ically in opposition to the stand of drys. (*Cf.* DRY, definition 1.)

WINO (*slang*). An alcoholic who drinks fortified wines to achieve intoxication at low cost, or who prefers wine for his intoxicating beverage.

Selected Reading List

Selected Reading List

BOOKS

AA MEMBERS. *Alcoholics Anonymous.* New York: Alcoholics Anonymous World Services, Inc., 1955.

The "bible" of AA members; the story of the way many thousands of men and women have recovered from alcoholism. The personal stories section is particularly interesting, including recoveries by people of diverse backgrounds—a housewife who drank at home, a great surgeon, a titled lady, a sculptor, and many more.

AL-ANON FAMILY GROUPS. *The Dilemma of the Alcoholic Marriage.* New York: Al-Anon Family Group Headquarters, Inc., 1967.

Highly useful to many spouses of alcoholics as well as to persons who counsel them. The experiences of wives, husbands, and family members of alcoholics who successfully resolved this crucial problem, not only through the permanent rehabilitation of the sick family member but in maintaining their own physical and mental well-being.

BILL W. *The AA Way of Life.* New York: Alcoholics Anonymous World Services, Inc., 1967.

Written by the fellowship's co-founder, this includes several hundred excerpts from the AA literature, touching nearly every aspect of AA's way of life. The short sections each contain a thought for individual meditation. An invaluable bedtable companion for a few minutes of relaxed reading for those intent on leading a happy and contented life without alcohol.

CLINEBELL, H. J. *Understanding and Counseling the Alcoholic.* New York. Abingdon Press, 1968.

Understanding and counseling the alcoholic through religion and psychology. The material on which parts I and II are based was taken from the writer's findings for his doctoral dissertation at Columbia University, entitled "Some Religious Approaches to the Problem of Alcoholism." Revised and enlarged.

THE COOPERATIVE COMMISSION ON THE STUDY OF ALCOHOLISM. *Alcohol Problems: A Report to the Nation.* Prepared by Thomas F. A. Plaut. New York: Oxford University Press, 1967.

The Commission, in five years' research under a grant from the National Institute of Mental Health, considered the entire range of alcohol problems in the United States—from public confusion and disagreement on the place of alcohol in society to the treatment and control of alcoholism by legal and educational means and by governmental and private agencies. In particular, the book deals with the history of alcohol use and of alcohol problems in America, with special emphasis on problem drinking. Shows the inadequacy of the treatment services presently available in this country.

FORD, J. C. *Depth Psychology, Morality and Alcoholism.* Weston, Mass.: Weston College Press, 1951.

An eminent Roman Catholic theologian considers the religious and moral implications of an addiction to alcohol. One conclusion is that the average alcoholic is sick in body, mind, and soul and usually cannot stop drinking without outside help. Cooperation with Alcoholics Anonymous, other professional men, and community agencies is essential to the successful pastoral care of alcoholics, Father Ford believes.

FOX, RUTH. *Alcoholism: Behavioral Research and Therapeutic Approaches.* New York: Springer Publishing Co., 1967.

Dr. Fox has presented a comprehensive picture of the most recent behavioral and therapeutic approaches to alcoholism. The volume begins with papers on research, moves to theory, and then to treatment; describes the role of other than medical personnel, includes the clergy and employers, and does not neglect the "skid row" problem.

JELLINEK, E. M. *The Disease Concept of Alcoholism.* Highland Park, New Jersey. Hillhouse Press, 1960.

"An honest publisher," Dr. Jellinek stated after completing this classic scientific treatise in the field of alcoholism, "would warn on the jacket of this book that temperance societies and the alcoholic beverage industry should not read it. It will not make them happy." Jellinek's original classification of "the alcoholisms" lays a foundation for a disease concept based on scientific principles. (Chapter 1 of the present book includes a digest of Jellinek's book.)

KELLER, MARK, and SEELEY, JOHN R. *The Alcohol Language: With a Selected Vocabulary.* Toronto, Canada: University of Toronto Press, 1958.

Both authors are equally concerned about the present terminological confusion and chaos in the field of alcohol problems. This monograph contains chapters on "The Language of Alcohol Problems" and "The Problems of Alcohol Language," together with a selected vocabulary (reprinted in the present book).

KENT, PATRICIA. *An American Woman and Alcohol.* New York: Holt, Rinehart & Winston, 1967.

A top woman executive in the communications field describes in simple terms the special considerations affecting a woman in relation to alcohol: how to tell if she is an alcoholic; how she became one; what alcohol will do to her looks, her emotional life, her job, her men, her children; how the unchecked use of tranquilizers and barbiturates speeds up the fatal results of alcoholism.

KINSEY, BARRY A. *The Female Alcoholic: A Social Psychological Study.* Springfield, Illinois: Charles C Thomas, 1966.

A study of alcoholism among women which makes full use of the concepts and methodological tools of the behavioral sciences. Based on the premise that alcoholism must be studied in the social and cultural contexts within which it occurs.

MC CARTHY, RAYMOND G. *Alcohol Education for Classroom and Community, A Source Book for Educators.* New York: McGraw-Hill, 1964.

Presents a comprehensive study of facts and attitudes regarding the use and non-use of alcoholic beverages and examines social concerns arising from excessive use. Since this is a source book for educators and college students, the material is as non-technical as possible. The late Mr. McCarthy made every effort to obtain objectivity in the discussion of controversial issues.

MANN, MARTY. *New Primer on Alcoholism.* New York: Holt, Rinehart & Winston, 1963.

This classic treatise for the layman tells how people drink, how to recognize alcoholism, and what to do about the problem. Mrs. Mann's book has helped thousands on the road back to a normal life and has sold over 50,000 copies. The author has been Executive Director of the National Council on Alcoholism for nearly a quarter of a century.

PITTMAN, DAVID J. *Society, Culture, and Drinking Patterns.* New York: John Wiley & Sons, Inc., 1962.

Research in alcoholism has progressed at such a rapid rate that it is difficult to keep abreast of recent advances and to compare studies in the variety of allied fields. This book aims to bring together a wide selection of the best current social-science research on drinking patterns, both normal and pathological.

TRICE, HARRISON M. *Alcoholism in America.* New York: McGraw-Hill, 1966.

Presents practical materials on alcoholism's impact on family and job, as well as an assessment of therapies and a discussion of prevention. A member of the faculty of Cornell University's School of Industrial and Labor Relations, Professor Trice has integrated extant data into a coherent social-psychological explanation of alcoholism in America. He considers alcohol a double-edged phenomenon, having both functional and disfunctional value.

WHITNEY, ELIZABETH D. *The Lonely Sickness.* Boston: Beacon Press, 1965.

Mrs. Whitney, for many years Executive Director of the Greater Boston Council on Alcoholism, states that alcoholism is a disease to which one in fourteen drinkers is susceptible because of a metabolic condition not unlike that which causes diabetes and, in some cases, excessive obesity. Like these diseases, the writer says, alcoholism requires professional and prolonged treatment as well as great determination on the part of the patient and the sympathetic and enlightened cooperation of his family.

PAMPHLETS

The following pamphlets can be obtained by writing the organizations mentioned.

Alcoholics and Their Families

AL-ANON FAMILY GROUP HEADQUARTERS, INC., P. O. Box 182, Madison Square Station, New York, N. Y. 10010:

Youth and the Alcoholic Parent (1960)
Counsels young people in adjusting their lives to an alcoholic situation in their homes. Prepared for Alateen, the section of the Al-Anon organization for young people seeking help for their own peace of mind and counseling for the alcoholic parent. A summary of many actual cases.

ALCOHOLICS ANONYMOUS WORLD SERVICES, INC., 305 East 45th Street, New York, N. Y. 10017:

The Alcoholic Husband (1954)
Brings a message of hope to wives whose husbands may or may not be interested in seeking help from AA. Based upon the experience of wives whose husbands found permanent and contented sobriety through AA therapy and way of life.

The Alcoholic Wife (1954)
Gives husbands facts about the AA approach to alcoholism, asks and answers many questions, and suggests ways in which husbands can help their wives, before and after the wives become members of AA.

Alcoholism—The Illness (1959)
Excerpts from talks on alcoholism as a disease made in 1944, 1949, and 1958, by Bill W., co-founder of AA. Contains a full explanation of the values in this modern approach compared with the former conceptions of alcoholism as a religious or moral problem.

Sedatives, Stimulants, and the Alcoholic (1964)
A report from a group of physicians who are also members of AA, on the way certain drugs may hurt as well as help. In recent years the "pill" problem has accentuated the complexities of recovery.

AMERICAN MEDICAL ASSOCIATION, 535 N. Dearborn St., Chicago, Ill. 60610:

Manual on Alcoholism (1967)

Although this manual by twelve medical authorities and one lay expert is intended to help physicians treat persons afflicted with alcoholism, it provides the general reader with knowledge of the development of the illness, its diagnosis, and its treatment.

NATIONAL COUNCIL ON ALCOHOLISM, 2 East 103rd Street, New York, N. Y. 10029:

The Alcoholic Spouse (1956)

By Ruth Fox, M. D. Discusses the role of the marriage partner in dealing with the complexities of the illness within the family circle.

Alcoholism: Nature of the Problem (reprinted 1964)

By Selden D. Bacon, Director of the Center of Alcohol Studies, Rutgers—The State University. Deals with current misconceptions of this disease, explains its compulsive and progressive nature and its inevitable development into chronic stages, and discusses its therapy and prevention.

Do's and Don'ts for the Wives of Alcoholics (1960)

Originally published by the North Carolina State Program for the Rehabilitation of Alcoholics. Stresses that the wife's solution lies in gaining knowledge of the problem. Particularly good are the sections on the futility of preaching and lecturing—or nagging—and reasoning, and on developing and maintaining a healthy emotional atmosphere in the home.

Facts on Alcoholism (revised 1966)

Statistics on the disease, including the nationwide prevalence and its economic costs. In connection with facilities for treatment, the publication states that the number of hospital beds, clinics, and personnel available for dealing with this vast public health problem are still "ridiculously inadequate."

A Guide for the Family of the Alcoholic (1960)

By Reverend Joseph L. Kellermann. An aid to the non-alcoholic members of the family when alcoholism develops. Originally published by Al-Anon.

THE CHRISTOPHER D. SMITHERS FOUNDATION, 405 Park Avenue, New York, N. Y. 10022:

Alcoholism—A Family Illness (1967)

The impact of alcoholism on family life, with suggestions on how all members of the family can work together to meet the crisis, motivate the alcoholic toward recovery, and make the necessary adustments in their own lives. (Parts of this pamphlet are included in Chapter 4 of the present book.)

The Alcoholism Complex (1960)

An analysis of the varieties of alcoholism. An abstract in laymen's language of *The Disease Concept of Alcoholism* by Dr. E. M. Jellinek. (Parts of this pamphlet are included in Chapter 1 of the present book.)

Arresting Alcoholism (1962)

Practical steps for the alcoholic, his family, his associates and his employer. (Parts of this pamphlet are included in Chapter 2 of the present book.)

Experimentation (1965)

An exposition of the dangers involved in any attempt at controlled or social drinking on the part of alcoholics. (Parts of this pamphlet are included in Chapter 3 of the present book.)

Alcohol Education for Young People

CLEVELAND HEALTH MUSEUM, CLEVELAND, OHIO:

What We Know About Alcohol (1957)

Mildred H. Weiss, a pioneer in teaching young people the modern approach to alcoholism as an illness, has written this manual for teachers and group leaders to accompany slides for alcohol education. Terse, succinct, and effective.

CONNECTICUT STATE DEPARTMENT OF MENTAL HEALTH, ALCOHOLISM DIVISION, 51 Coventry Street, Hartford, Conn.:

Teaching about Alcohol in Connecticut Schools (1966)

This publication is a complete revision of an earlier education bulletin. The State Department of Education cooperates in emphasizing the importance of questions about drinking for today's boys and girls and the need for educators to have sound, acceptable, and effective approaches. Particularly interesting are the evaluation techniques, entitled "How're We Doing?"

MISSISSIPPI STATE DEPARTMENT OF EDUCATION, Jackson, Miss.:

Alcohol Education Handbook. Mississippi School Bulletin No. 141.

A guide to assist secondary-school administrators and teachers in organizing a program of alcohol education with emphasis on the value of developing attitudes of constructive inquiry and forthright analysis. The objective is to help the student acquire a sense of responsibility toward himself and his community in relation to various undesirable aspects of the use of alcoholic beverages. Aids the student in making the necessary adjustments in later life.

NATIONAL COUNCIL ON ALCOHOLISM, 2 East 103rd Street, New York, N. Y. 10029:

Alcohol and the Adolescent

A reprint of an article in *Parents' Magazine,* by Jean Libman Block. The section devoted to parents is especially useful. For all of us, says Miss Block, alcohol presents one of today's greatest unsolved problems, but as parents we do know that our children will look to us for guidance in this matter of drinking. Delineates ways of achieving proper guidance.

Could Your Child Become an Alcoholic? (1960)

By Marvin A. Block, M. D., former chairman of the Committee on Alcoholism of the American Medical Association. Teenagers are in danger unless their parents know the facts about drinking, Dr. Block warns. His advice can prevent a family tragedy.

Discussion Guides for Questions About Alcohol (1956)

By the late Raymond G. McCarthy, Rutgers University Center of Alcohol Studies. Establishes significant guideposts relating to the physiological effects of alcohol. The section on physiological dependence is clearly explained for adolescent understanding.

Exploring Alcohol Questions (1962)

This brochure contains inserts to be taken out for individual study. The subjects include: "American Attitudes Toward Drinking," "Action of Alcohol in the Body," "Alcohol and Highway Safety," "Alcoholism and the Alcoholic," and "Topics for Further Study." Prepared for secondary-school classroom use by the late

Raymond G. McCarthy, Rutgers University Center of Alcohol Studies.

What Shall Our Schools Teach About Alcohol? (1964)

By Raymond G. McCarthy; originally published in the *National Parent Teachers Magazine.* Warns parents and teachers that alcohol education, like sex education, is no simple task, since it involves attitudes as well as facts. How much of the burden of such education can we put on our public schools? What are some of the questions that will have to be answered—and by whom— before the schools can do an effective job?

What Shall We Tell Our Children About Drinking? (1960)

By John Park Lee. A prominent churchman advises parents on guiding young people toward a decision about the use of alcoholic beverages. Alcohol is everywhere in American life today, the writer points out, stating that there is ample evidence that the overwhelming majority of persons who drink had their first drink before leaving high school. While children sometimes do listen to what their parents say, they pay much closer attention to what parents *do.* Consequently parents must remember that their attitudes toward alcohol must be realistic in the social pattern of today's living.

OREGON STATE MENTAL HEALTH DIVISION, ALCOHOL STUDIES & REHABILITA-TION SECTION, 10 N. W. 10th Avenue, Portland, Ore.:

Alcohol Education in Oregon Schools (1964)

By George C. Dimas, currently (1968) president of the North American Association of Alcoholism Programs, which comprises more than 40 programs on alcoholism in various states and Canadian provinces. An excellent topic outline and resource unit for teachers, widely used in Oregon schools and colleges, this booklet brings to bear scientific information on alcoholism and the entire gamut of behavior related to alcohol usage.

Industry and Alcoholism

KEMPER INSURANCE COMPANY, 4750 Sheridan Road, Chicago, Ill. 60640:

A Neglected Area of Loss Reduction: What to do About the Employee with a Drinking Problem (1966)

An aid to business and industry, showing how excessive costs can be reduced and valued employees retained through policies and procedures which utilize current knowledge about the disease of alcoholism.

METROPOLITAN LIFE INSURANCE COMPANY, 1 Madison Ave., New York, N. Y. 10010:

Alcoholism (1967)

Outlines what alcoholism is, what causes it, the kinds of treatment available. Includes a section on Alcoholics Anonymous.

THE NATIONAL COUNCIL ON ALCOHOLISM, 2 East 103rd St., New York, N. Y. 10007:

The Modern Approach to Alcoholism (1965)

By Lewis F. Presnall. A general education pamphlet for employees which furnishes a basic understanding of the disease concept of alcoholism. A questionnaire is included to enable the employee to determine the approximate stage of the progression of alcoholism. Explodes five popular myths concerning alcoholism.

NATIONAL INDUSTRIAL CONFERENCE BOARD, 845 Third Ave., New York, N. Y.

The Alcoholic Worker (1958)

A pioneer round-up of information on the programs on alcoholism then in existence. Written for management, this is still useful for its detailed presentation of the successful operation of a company program, giving specific examples among well-known companies.

THE CHRISTOPHER D. SMITHERS FOUNDATION, 405 Park Avenue, New York, N. Y. 10022:

Alcoholism in Industry—Modern Procedures (1962)

By Professor Harrison M. Trice, School of Industrial and Labor Relations, Cornell University. A survey of the basic problems of handling alcoholism among employees as an illness. For all levels of management from top executives to foremen.

A Company Program on Alcoholism—Basic Outline (1959)

Prepared by the Smithers Foundation with the help of 34 companies which have such programs in effect, as an aid to management in formulating a policy for rehabilitating alcoholic employees. This outline has had wide circulation in industrial management circles.

WESTERN ELECTRIC COMPANY, 195 Broadway, New York, N. Y. 10007:

Policy and Program—Employees with Drinking Problems (A Guide for Supervisors) (1962)

Prepared as a guide for the company's supervisory personnel to enable them to participate intelligently in its program for rehabilitation of alcoholic employees. Useful for all company management people.

Alcoholism Information for Professionals

THE CHRISTOPHER D. SMITHERS FOUNDATION, 405 Park Ave., New York, N. Y. 10022:

Alcohol and Alcoholism: A Police Handbook (1966)

A handbook prepared by the Correctional Association of New York, the International Association of Chiefs of Police, and the Smithers Foundation to provide law enforcement officers with a good understanding of alcohol, its uses and abuses and its relationship with the law. Presently in wide use among state law enforcement bodies, the judiciary and legislators. (Parts of this handbook are included in Chapter 8 of the present book.)

Biochemical and Nutritional Aspects of Alcoholism (1964)

A summation of lectures delivered by well-known authorities on two neglected aspects of alcoholism. Some scientists predict that the greatest progress in getting at the fundamental causes of alcoholism will come over the next decade in the pharmocological and biochemical fields. Malnutrition plays an important role in the development of alcoholism and proper nutrition is essential in the rehabilitation period of treatment. (Three of the lectures are reprinted in condensed form in Chapter 4 of the present book.)

Guide Lines for Admission of Alcoholics to Hospitals (1968)

Many alcoholism authorities believe that the greatest barrier to widespread prevention of alcoholism is the failure on the part of hospitals to accept patients under the diagnosis of alcoholism. Many boards of directors and medical heads who set the admittance policies of the nation's hospitals are still doubtful of the status of alcoholism as a disease. This pamphlet contains the recommendations of the American Medical Association and the American

Hospital Association for admission of alcoholic patients, as well as the recent guide lines for the hospitalization of alcoholic patients, prepared for the Medical Society of the State of New York by Marvin A. Block, M. D.

Index

Index

21